The Science an

Model and Object Drawing

A text book for schools and for self-instruction
of teachers and art students in the theory and
practice of drawing from objects

Lucas Baker

Alpha Editions

This edition published in 2020

ISBN : 9789354004674

Design and Setting By
Alpha Editions
email - alphaedis@gmail.com

WHITE'S INDUSTRIAL DRAWING

THE SCIENCE AND ART

OF

MODEL AND OBJECT DRAWING

A Text-Book for Schools

AND FOR SELF-INSTRUCTION OF TEACHERS AND ART-STUDENTS
IN THE THEORY AND PRACTICE OF DRAWING
FROM OBJECTS

BY

LUCAS BAKER

Art-Master

FORMERLY SUPERVISOR OF DRAWING IN THE PUBLIC SCHOOLS OF THE
CITY OF BOSTON

ILLUSTRATED

CONTENTS.

3

CONTENTS.

INTRODUCTION.

HE tendency of the American people to study art marks an era in our intellectual life. Students of art multiply rapidly : art-schools are well filled, and private teachers are in great demand. All branches of art are receiving attention, and especially the industrial department.

There are two sources of art-instruction, — the *teacher*, and *nature*. There are also two methods of practice, — working from copies, and working from nature. Multitudes of private pupils do nothing but copy the work of others, and consequently they never acquire the power to produce original work themselves. The two methods may be combined, but nature must always be regarded as the great instructor. We can do no greater service to our pupils than to prepare them to learn from nature, to open their eyes and minds to the harmonies and melodies which she has in ample store for them.

There is no department of public instruction better adapted to the development of the powers of observation than drawing from objects.

The art-student, in progressing through the various branches of his study, is soon confronted with the necessity of making for himself original drawings from objects. He can not long follow copies, and depend upon them for guidance : he must read forms independently, as he would read a book ; and he must give his own rendering of them.

At this stage he is presumed to have acquired a ready hand in drawing from the copy, and to be in possession of some knowledge of Plane Geometry. Thus prepared he enters upon a tour of investigation, not unlike the explorer of a new country. He must note all the facts presented to his observation, and deduce all the laws discoverable by his understanding.

To the student it is emphatically a *field* of discovery. His eyes must be opened to new facts, which have been hitherto unnoticed by him. His method of seeing is to be changed from the casual and accidental to the accurate and discriminating method which penetrates and comprehends the subtleties of the apparent forms of objects, and of light, shade, shadow, reflections, and color. Every teacher of art knows that the principal part of his work is teaching his pupils *to see* and *how to see.* The pupil begins with little knowledge of the apparent forms of objects, and with no habit of observing them. This knowledge must be acquired, and the habit of seeing must be formed. This is the only foundation for true progress. In this respect, *to draw is to know; and not to know, is not to be able to draw.*

The subject of Object-Drawing has a basis of fact throughout. There is no guess-work ; mathematical precision pervades the whole ; every question can be settled by reference to fundamental principles.

Model-drawing is the best possible preparation for sketching from nature. The student graduating from the study of models goes fully equipped to the delineation of natural scenery or of architectural objects. Without this preparation the results of his efforts would be uncertain, and accurate only by accident. It furnishes the scientific basis for *free sketching;* and without it, and an understanding of its principles, no artist can count himself secure in his work.

The first part of model-drawing, viz., that relating to apparent forms, is closely related to Descriptive Geometry; while the second part, viz., light, shade, shadow, and reflection, falls within the province of the fixed laws of light. The third division, viz., color, has also its fixed limitations and conditions: hence the whole field of our subject falls within the domain of *science*, and only partially within that of *taste*.

The models used in this department are geometrical forms, and objects based on these, as the sphere, cylinder, cone, cube, prism, pyramid, plinths, vases, rings, etc., supplemented by numerous objects of utility and beauty, whose forms bear close relationship to geometrical types. To become thoroughly familiar with the principles of the whole subject should be the aim of every student of pictorial or industrial art; for thus only will the way become clear for any future advancement.

Model-drawing also possesses an educational value that ought to commend it to every true teacher. The general tendency of the course of instruction in the public schools, aside from drawing, is toward the development of the world of ideas, and not toward the development of the power of observation. Indeed, so strongly is this the case, that the mind is drawn away from the real, visible, and tangible, to the contemplation of the unseen and ideal. Thus our pupils come to belong to the class, that, "*having eyes, see not.*" We say, then, that the discipline derived from the practice of this subject tends to put the pupil in full possession of his faculties.

Emerson says, "The study of art is of high value to the growth of the intellect ;" and Goethe called drawing "That most moral of all accomplishments," saying, "It unfolds and necessitates attention, and that is the highest of all skills and virtues."

Attention makes the scholar, the want of it the dunce.

It is said that the artist knows what to look for, and what he sees ; and it is almost equally true, that the untrained in model and object drawing do not know what to look for, or what they see. It is for *these reasons* that our subject has a high educational utility over and above all considerations of its industrial or commercial value. Model-drawing in particular, and drawing in general, should be well taught in our public schools, in order to secure a more complete development of the mental powers.

Moreover, this subject opens to the pupil new sources of enjoyment ; as it unfolds new powers, and extends the area of his mental vision, while it increases the value of his labor in life. The power he derives from it enters into all skills and labors, and adds another segment to the arc of his being.

The student has presented to his mind, for his comprehension, a multitudinous series of facts relating to form, light and shade, shadow and reflection. The whole series must be appropriated and digested, and made a part of the student : he must assimilate the whole if he would attain to a complete mastery of the subject. The best method for the teacher to follow, is to place before his pupils a single model, and then, — first, to lead them carefully to recognize the several facts, relations, and principles involved in its apparent form ; secondly, to note the distribution of light, shade, shadow, and reflection on the same ; and, thirdly, to deduce the general principles which the observation and comparison of these appearances are found to establish.

It is not enough merely to set the pupil to work on the models. His powers of observation are undeveloped, and need directing. At the same time, the rules should be deduced by the pupil, and not furnished ready-made by the teacher. The pupil should be taken into partnership with the teacher in the analysis of the subject, and taught to write down his own conclusions. He will thus appropriate and assimilate the facts for his own use, so that he will feel he is in full possession of them.

The practice in all branches of our school instruction should be to lead and direct the pupil's minds in all their investigations, rather than to impose upon them a burden of arbitrary dogmatism without regard to their power of assimilation.

In the practice of model or object drawing we place the objects before us in suitable positions, and proceed to draw them with pencil, brush, or crayon, in line, light, and shade, or in color, as we may choose. The method is wholly a freehand process throughout : we use no instruments but the pencil, brush, stump, and rubber ; and we proceed upon certain general and fundamental principles which are to be noticed hereafter, to make the representation upon whatever surfaces we may have chosen for that purpose. Model and Object Drawing, then, is a study for the artist as well as for the mechanic.

In Perspective Drawing, which is really a branch of Descriptive Geometry applied to the representation of objects as they appear, we make a drawing of an object or objects wholly or mainly with instruments for measurement and execution, following certain fixed and determined laws of intersection of lines and planes, from certain assumed or fixed data or measurements, upon whatever plane surface we may have selected for that purpose.

It is a mechanical and not a freehand process : hence it is not the ordinary method followed by the artist in securing his " views," but it is generally the method employed by the architect to render apparent the results of his inventions and combinations.

It will be seen, therefore, that, in practice, Object Drawing and Perspective Drawing are essentially different.   But, however different the practice in these two departments may be, there are certain fundamental principles common to both ; and they are in complete harmony, the one with the other.   If there seem to be contradictions, they are apparent only, and not real, and are owing to a want of understanding of the subjects under consideration.

MODEL AND OBJECT DRAWING.

TERMS AND DEFINITIONS.

HE terms used in drawing, so far as they relate to mathematical quantities, should be identical with those used in Geometry; and they should be given the same value.

It may be useful, therefore, to insert here a partial analysis of geometrical quantities, with their definitions, for the use of those who are not otherwise familiar with the same.

A class of beginners should be taught to distinguish and to define geometrical quantities as a preparation for model or perspective drawing. Let them begin with the four kinds of geometrical quantities, and learn to refer any quantity to its own class: this is the first step in getting at the correct definition.

In Geometry there are four different kinds of quantities, sometimes called quantities of different degrees.

First, Quantities of Length: all lines belong to this degree.

Second, Quantities of Surface: all surfaces belong to this degree.

Third, Quantities of Volume: all solids belong to this degree.

Fourth, Quantities of Inclination: all angles belong to this degree.

11

The degree, or kind, to which any quantity belongs determines the first word or words of the definition of that quantity. The last part of the definition refers to the manner of limitation or boundary.

OF LIMITS.

Points limit lines, lines limit surfaces, surfaces limit volumes; or, to reverse the statement, we should have these limitations in the following order: volumes are limited by surfaces, surfaces are limited by lines, and lines are limited by points.

Or again: quantities of the first degree, or kind, are limited by points; quantities of the second degree are limited by quantities of the first degree; and quantities of the third degree are limited by quantities of the second degree.

Quantities of the fourth degree are limited by lines or planes.

OF EXTENSION.

Extension is ultimately the occupation of space. Extension has three dimensions, — length (lines), breadth (surface), thickness (limited space or volume).

A *POINT* is the zero of extension, as it possesses neither of the three elements of extension: hence it is position only.

QUANTITIES OF THE FIRST DEGREE.—LINES.

There are straight, curved, broken, and mixed lines.

A *STRAIGHT LINE* is the direct distance between two points. A straight line is one without change of direction.

A *CURVED LINE* is one in which the direction is constantly chan-
ging. The change of direction is constant, or constantly increasing
or diminishing by a certain law of ratio; or it may be irregular. A
curved line may lie wholly in a plane, or in a regularly curved surface,
or in an irregularly curved surface.

QUANTITIES OF THE SECOND DEGREE.—SURFACES.

Surfaces are of several kinds, such as regularly curved surfaces, —
those of the sphere, cylinder, cones, etc.; rolling and wrinkled surfaces; broken and warped surfaces; and surfaces which are neither
warped, broken, nor curved in any direction, but are straight in all
directions: these last are called **Planes.**

A *PLANE*, therefore, is any straight surface. Planes are considered
infinite if not limited; and lines limit planes, as stated above. A
plane takes its name from the manner of its limitation. Thus, when
a plane is limited by a curved line, every point of which is equally
distant from a point within the plane, the plane is called a **Circle.**

A *CIRCLE*, then, is a plane limited by a curved line, every point of
which is equally distant from a certain point within the plane called
the center. (It will be observed here, that the distinction between the
plane of the circle and its limiting line is kept clearly in view.)

Again, a plane limited by three straight lines is called a **Triangle:**
therefore, a *TRIANGLE* is a plane limited by three
straight lines. Triangles are of five kinds. **Right-
angle** triangles (Fig. A), having one right angle;
Right-angle Isosceles triangles, having a right angle
and two equal sides (Fig. B); **Equilateral** triangles, having the three

sides equal (Fig. C) ; **Isosceles,** having two sides equal (Fig. D) ; and **Scalene,** having the three sides and angles unequal (Fig. E).

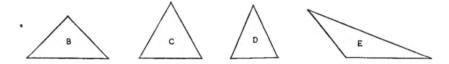

From the same analogy we should have the following definitions of planes.

A *SQUARE* is a plane limited by four equal straight lines, which make four right angles one with another.

A *RECTANGLE* is a plane limited by four straight lines, the opposite lines being equal, and forming four right angles.

A *RHOMBUS* is a plane limited by four equal straight lines, having only its opposite angles equal.

A *RHOMBOID* is a plane limited by four straight lines, only the opposite lines being equal, and forming equal opposite angles.

A *REGULAR PENTAGON* is a plane limited by five equal straight lines forming five equal angles.

A *REGULAR HEXAGON* is a plane limited by six equal straight lines forming six equal angles.

A *REGULAR HEPTAGON* is a plane limited by seven equal straight lines forming seven equal angles.

A *REGULAR OCTAGON* is a plane limited by eight equal straight lines forming eight equal angles.

A *REGULAR NONAGON* is a plane limited by nine equal straight lines forming nine equal angles.

A *REGULAR DECAGON* is a plane limited by ten equal straight lines forming ten equal angles.

An *ELLIPSE* is a plane limited by a curved line, every point of which is equal in the sum of its distances from two points within the plane called the *foci*. An ellipse is said to have two axes, or diameters: they are at right angles to each other; and they are called the major and minor axis, or, in common language, the longer and the shorter diameters.

Returning to the circle and its different parts and their limitations, the definition of each part is dependent upon the kind of quantity to which it belongs. Thus, the *CIRCUMFERENCE* is the line of limitation; and the *CIRCLE* is the *plane* limited. The circumference becomes the figure of the circle. A part of the circumference of a circle is called an **Arc** (Fig. 1).

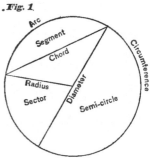

Fig. 1.

The *SEMICIRCLE* is the *half-plane* of the circle limited by the semi-circumference and the subtending diameter.

A *SECTOR* is a part of the *plane* of a circle limited by two radii and the included arc.

A *SEGMENT* is a part of the plane of a circle limited by an arc and its chord. It will be observed, that, in the foregoing definitions of the several limited planes, the word *"figure"* is not used. It seems that this word tends to confusion; preventing, in some cases, the mind from seizing at once the idea. We may say that every limited plane has a figure, but the figure is not the plane: the circle has a figure; yet the figure of a circle is not the circle, but the perimeter, or circumference, of the circle.   We can never find the area of a figure ; because the figure is only outline, and not area at all. All figures, as such, belong to quantities of the first degree.

QUANTITIES OF THE THIRD DEGREE.—VOLUMES.

Extending on all sides of us, above and below, is the infinite space of the universe in which all worlds and beings have their existence. Whenever any portion of this infinite unlimited space becomes limited in any manner, such portion of space becomes a volume : therefore, —

A *VOLUME* is any limited portion of space, and the volume takes its name from the method of its limitation.

A *SPHERE* is a *volume* limited by a curved surface, every point of which is equally distant from the center of the sphere.

A *CUBE* is a volume limited by six equal squares.

A *PYRAMID* is a volume limited by a polygon and as many equal isosceles triangles as the polygon has sides.

A *CONE* is a volume limited, both by a circle as a base, and a curved surface which is straight in the directions of all lines drawn from the circumference of the base to a point in a line perpendicular to the center of the circle, called the Apex; or a cone would be limited as described by the revolution of a right-angle triangle about one of its sides adjacent to the right angle.

A *CYLINDER* is a volume limited by two opposite equal and parallel circles, and by a surface curved in the direction of the circumferences of the circles, and straight at right angles to this direction.

A *PRISM* is a volume limited by two equal, opposite, and parallel polygons, and as many equal rectangles as either of the polygons has sides.

QUANTITIES OF THE FOURTH DEGREE. – INCLINATION.

When two lines in the same plane incline to each other, the inclination is called an **Angle.** Angles are of three kinds, **Right Angles** (Fig. F), **Acute Angles** (Fig. G), and **Obtuse Angles** (Fig. H). When

one line meets another line, forming two equal angles on the same side of the line met, both angles are **Right Angles.** The point of intersection of two lines forming an angle is called the **Vertex** of the angle. There may be four right angles in the same plane having their vertices in the same point. An **Acute Angle** is less than a right angle. An **Obtuse Angle** is greater than a right angle. The inclination of two planes also forms an *angle.* The inclination and intersection of three or more planes, at one point, form a **Solid Angle.**

WORDS DENOTING POSITION AND RELATION.

Two other classes of definitions are important to the student; viz., those of words which denote position, and those of words which denote relation.

First, Words denoting position; namely, **vertical, horizontal, level, flat, inclined.** All these terms signify position, without relation to any other object save the earth itself. That is to say, a line in any of these positions is so of itself alone, without the aid of any other line.

Second, Words denoting relation ; namely, **parallel, perpendicular, tangent, secant,** etc. A line in any of these positions bears a certain definite relation to some other line, and changes position with such line. A *PARALLEL LINE* is one which is everywhere equally distant from another line ; while a *vertical* line is vertical alone, and of itself, from its position only.

A *VERTICAL LINE* is one in an upright position, pointing to the center of the earth.

A *HORIZONTAL LINE* is one, all points of which are on the same level. A horizontal line drawn through any point is perpendicular to a vertical line drawn through the same point, and the vertical is perpendicular to the horizontal line.

An *INCLINED LINE* is one, all points of which are at different elevations.

A line is perpendicular to another line when it makes a right angle with it.

A line is *tangent* to another line when it touches it at a single point, and would not cut it if both were produced.

ORTHOGRAPHIC PROJECTIONS.

In order to understand clearly some of the illustrations and descriptions which follow in this book, we think it advisable to ask the attention of the student to a brief preliminary statement of the leading principles and methods of Orthographic Projection. The object of these projections is, to show the *real* forms of objects, or combinations of objects ; so that any one understanding these methods

of representation can construct from such drawings the things represented. These methods are generally used by architects, machinists,
ship-builders, and inventors, to represent in detail the forms, dimensions, combinations, and methods of action, of whatever they may
invent or design. They are also useful in demonstrating many geometrical principles, with reference to perspective, forms of shadows,
intersections of solids, etc.

Two planes of projection at right angles to each other are em
ployed. One of these is named the *Vertical* plane of *Projection,*
the projection itself on this plane being generally called the *Elevation :* the other plane is named the *Horizontal* plane of *Projection,* and
the projection on it is called the *Plan.* The plan and elevation of a
building or machine, drawn to dimensions, gives an idea of its form,
size, and method of construction. Two or more vertical or horizontal
projections may be drawn where they are required to determine additional details. By these means the most complicated combinations
can be made apparent.

The use we shall make of these
methods will be to show the apparent
forms of some objects, and to demon-
strate certain mathematical principles.

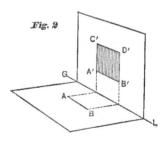

Fig. 2

Let us suppose that we have, as in
Fig. 2, two planes represented by sheets of
paper at right angles to each other, — one
in a vertical, and the other in a horizontal,
position, intersecting or touching each other in the line G L. These
planes are represented in a perspective view, and we will say they are
each one foot square. Let us suppose, further, that the sun is in the

west. Place the vertical plane so the sun's rays will strike the plane at right angles to its surface, while they pass parallel to the horizontal plane.

Now, if we hold a four-inch square plane, or piece of paper, parallel to the vertical plane, at a little distance from it, with two of its sides vertical, the paper will throw upon the vertical plane a shadow which will have the precise form and dimensions of the four-inch square. We may call this shadow the vertical projection of the square.

With the square in the same position, suppose the sun directly over-head : the horizontal projection of the square will be cast down upon the horizontal plane.

This projection is a straight line, four inches long. In the figure the vertical projection of the square is the square A′ B′ C′ D′, and its horizontal projection in the same position is the straight line A B.

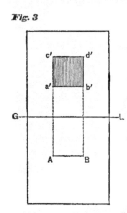

Fig. 3

It is not customary to represent, as above, these planes of projection in a perspective view, but simply to draw a horizontal line on the paper, representing the intersection of the vertical and the horizontal planes, and to regard that part of the paper above the line as the vertical plane, and that part below the line as the horizontal plane. This line is called the ground-line, and it is marked with the letters G L.

Let us analyze the case above described (Fig. 3). Rays of light moving in horizontal parallel lines, perpendicular to the vertical plane above the line G L, cause the shadow of the square to fall upon that plane ; and rays of light moving vertically downward, in parallel lines, cause the shadow of the square to be cast on the horizontal plane. The first shadow is a square, and the second is a line. Hence, when we see the two elements projected, we know of what form they are the projections: since the horizontal projection is only a line, we see that the object which is the origin of projection must be merely a plane, because it possesses no appreciable thickness; and, since we have a square for the vertical projection, we know that the plane is in the form of a square. Thus we are able to understand the form of an object from its projections.

By observing still further the two projections, we should also see what position the object occupies with reference to both planes. Since A B is parallel to the ground-line, we know that the square is parallel to the vertical plane ; and, when we see that A'B' is parallel to the ground-line, we know that the lower and upper edges are parallel to the horizontal plane.

In Figs. 4 and 5 the horizontal and vertical projections of several solids are shown.

First, we have the sphere at A ; having, for its horizontal and vertical projections, a circle. It is, of course, the same in both : but it should be observed that two circles at right angles to each other, and intersecting at the horizontal diameter of each, would give the same projections ; but, if these planes were revolved into different positions, as in Figs. C E H and K, the projections would show that they were planes, and not a sphere.

At B we have the projections of a cube. Two squares at right angles to each other would give the same projections. At C we have the cube revolved on the horizontal plane, so as to bring one diagonal of the upper and lower sides perpendicular to the vertical plane.

In this position, two square planes would not give the horizontal and
vertical projections of the solid, as at C. In this figure we observe
that the horizontal projection gives the true form and dimensions
of a side of the cube, and that the vertical projection does neither.

At D we have the horizontal and vertical projections of a cone, —
the horizontal being a circle equal to the base of the cone; and the
vertical projection, a triangle equal to a vertical section through the
axis of the cone.

At E we have the same tipped up, with its base and axis oblique

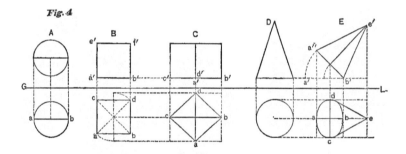

to the horizontal plane. This projection is made by revolving, on the
point b' as a center, $a'\,b'$ in its horizontal position on the vertical
plane, to the position $a''\,b'$; on this as a base constructing the triangle.
The horizontal projection of the same is made by carrying forward to
the right, from D to E, the diameter $c\,d$; letting fall the dotted ver-
ticals from $a''\,b'$ to determine $a\,b$. It is evident that this latter diameter, $a\,b$, will be foreshortened. Upon these two diameters, the
horizontal projection of the circle must be drawn: it will be an ellipse.
The dotted vertical, let fall from the apex e', will give the place of the

vertex *e* in the horizontal projection. From this point draw tangents to the ellipse, and the figure will be complete.

At F we have the projections of a four-sided pyramid: the vertical projection is a triangle, equal to a vertical section through the axis and diameter of the base.

The horizontal shows the projection of the base: and the four isosceles triangles, in their oblique positions, forming the sides of the pyramid, are projected at *a b e*, *b e c*, *c e d*, *d e a ;*

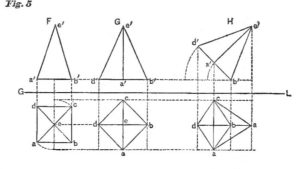

Fig. 5

each having the common point *e*. The projections of its oblique position at H are obtained similarly to those of the cone, after first constructing its projections at G, where it has been revolved on the horizontal plane through a quarter circumference.

At I, J, K (Fig. 6), we have, in succession, the projections of a four-sided prism in several positions. At I the sides of the prism are perpendicular, and parallel to the vertical plane; at J the prism has been revolved so as to bring the sides at an angle of 45° to the vertical plane; and, at K, it is tipped up so that the bases and sides make angles with the horizontal plane. The method of drawing these projections will be readily understood by what has preceded.

The reader will further observe, that the projection of any particular line or plane may be studied from these projections of solids.

For instance, at I the edge of the prism, represented by the line *e′ a′* in the vertical projection, has its horizontal projection in the point *a ;* and in the same way the remaining edges, represented by the other vertical lines in the vertical projection, have their horizontal projections in their corresponding points. We conclude, therefore, from what was found in the case of the four-inch square, and in the present investigation, that *the vertical projection of a vertical line* is *a vertical line*

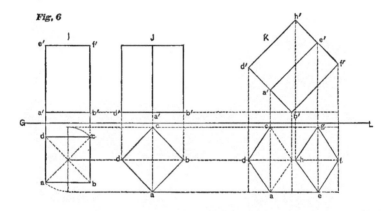

Fig. 6

of the same length, and that the horizontal projection of a vertical line is a point.

If we take the lines, *a d, b c,* at I, in the horizontal projection, which are the projections of the two opposite sides of both bases of the prism, the bases being perpendicular to the vertical plane, we see that their vertical projections are found in the points *a′, e′, b′, f′.* Therefore, we conclude *that the horizontal projection of a horizontal line is a straight line of the same length ; and, if the line is perpendicular to the vertical plane, its vertical projection will be a point.* By examination of the several planes bounding this solid, we see that the horizontal bases are projected on the horizontal plane in squares of the same size, since, in all these projections, the rays are assumed to be parallel ; and that also the two side planes, which are parallel to the vertical plane, are projected in rectangles of the same magnitude. We may say, then, *that, when a plane is parallel to either plane of projection, its projection on that plane will be equal to the plane itself.*

If we examine the front face of the prism, as projected in $a'\,b'\,f'\,e'$, we see that it has its horizontal projection in the line $a\,b$, and the other three sides of the prism have their horizontal projections in the lines $b\,c,\,c\,d,\,d\,a\,;$ the two bases have their horizontal projection in $a\,b\,c\,d$, and their vertical projection in the lines $a'\,b'$ and $e'\,f'$: hence, *whenever a plane is perpendicular to either plane of projection, its projection on that plane will be a straight line.*

In J we have the vertical planes of the prism in their oblique positions projected on the vertical plane ; and we see, comparing them with the vertical projections in I, that neither projection is of the same size as the plane itself: but, in the horizontal projection, we have the two bases of the prism projected in their true form and dimensions. Compare with $a\,b\,c\,d$ in I.

By comparing K with I and J, we see that none of the planes limiting the solid are shown in their true dimensions. The analysis of this subject might be carried on to any extent, and deductions made, and processes developed, for showing various combinations and forms, intersections of solids, projections of shadows, principles of construction, etc. ; but we have given enough of the principles of Orthographic Projections to enable the attentive student to understand the illustrations given in the body of the book. This is all that is necessary for our present purpose.

HOW TO READ APPARENT FORMS.

If one had the faculty, when looking at a house, for example, of making it appear like a flat spot of a certain shape, disregarding the

fact that certain surfaces are retreating, thus reducing the whole to one vertical plane, he would have the most complete qualification for rapid sketching (Fig. 7). Indeed, this is just what the artist endeavors, as far as possi- ble, to do in order to read forms. It is not difficult to read off rapidly the outline after the whole complex arrange- ment of planes, constituting the house, or the group of buildings, has been reduced to one plane. But our *knowledge* of the retreating of the planes, and of their many combinations, makes it very hard to secure the apparent form of the whole group.

Herein our *knowledge* of real forms and directions seems to stand in the way of our appreciation of other facts relating to appearances ; so that it always happens that the beginner draws the forms as he knows them to exist, instead of representing them only as they appear to his eye. *To draw what you see, to paint what you see, and not what your knowledge leads you to imagine you see,* must be the constant admonition of the teacher. Works of imagination may be excellent, and greatly to be prized ; but, at this stage, neither the imagination nor the knowledge of the pupil is of any avail. He must depend only upon his eyes. Seeing with the eyes, and knowing from data in the mind, are very different acts; and the province of each is separate from that of the other.

Taking the cube with three faces visible, if we can make the whole block appear like a flat spot on a vertical plane when seen horizontally, we can then draw the various lines with accuracy by referring each to an imaginary horizontal or vertical, passing through one end of the same, and by noting the angle (Fig. 8). The inclination of all lines may be determined by reference to the vertical or to the horizontal.

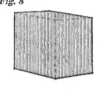

Fig. 8

To sum up these suggestions, we say that all attempts at comparison of lengths and positions of lines must be made on a plane perpendicular to the axis of sight, or, in other words, perpendicular to the central ray from the object to be drawn. A common way is, to hold out the pencil at arm's-length, in such a position that one end is as near to the eye as the other, and then to

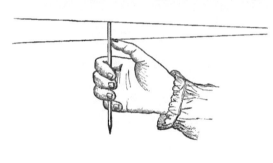

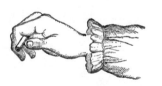

compare two lines as to their apparent lengths, or their positions with regard to each other, or to a horizontal or a vertical line. Thus, relative apparent lengths, and relative apparent positions, may be determined.   See cut of hands showing the positions of the pencil.

A very satisfactory and conclusive method of testing the accuracy of a drawing of a simple object, after it is made, is to cut out the drawing with a pen-knife, running the point around the outside, or the outer lines of the whole figure, and folding back the different planes on certain lines.   Thus, in the case of the cube, Fig. 9, run the knife along the full lines, and fold back the several squares on the dotted

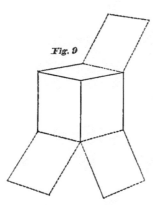

Fig. 9

lines, and then hold the paper at such a distance from the eye that the model from which the drawing was made will appear to just fill the opening.   Any error in the work will be seen at once.   In the same way the drawing of any separate plane may be tested by putting in place all the other planes, leaving the one to be determined folded back. Care must be taken to hold the paper in a position perpendicular to the central ray from the object to the eye.

A very simple method of finding the apparent position of a line, when neither horizontal nor vertical, is to hold out the pencil as above directed, so as to coincide with the line to be determined, and, with the other hand holding up the paper, bring the pencil against it in a position corresponding to that of the line.   The direction of the line on the paper will thus be readily determined. The pupil may also put up in front of the eye a plate of glass, and, holding the head fixed in one position, may trace upon it the outline of the object.

THE DIASCOPE.

The *DIASCOPE* is a simple contrivance for testing apparent forms.

This instrument is simply a frame, across which are drawn fine wires or threads, at equal distances, in two opposite directions, dividing the space inclosed into a number of equal squares. A frame four inches square, inside measure, is a convenient size. The frame should be made of some thin material, and provided with a handle. The

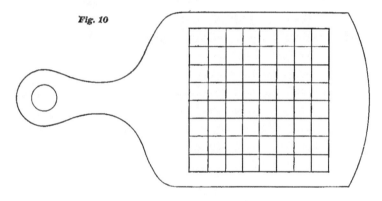

Fig. 10

inner lines of the frame may then be divided into half-inch spaces, and small holes should be made near the inner edges at the points of division. Small wires or threads may be drawn through these holes from opposite sides, dividing the whole space, for instance, into sixty-four equal squares.

When completed, the Diascope may be held up in a vertical position, between the object to be drawn and the eye, so that the central ray of light from the object will pass through the Diascope at right angles to its plane. With it in this position, the observer will be enabled to read off without difficulty many of the apparent inclinations and magnitudes.

The side of a cigar-box, and two or three yards of fine iron or copper wire, is all the material required in the construction of this instrument (Fig. 10).

ANALYSIS OF APPARENT FORMS.

Every visible object transmits to the eye of the observer rays of light from every part of its visible surface. The rays of light move in straight lines and converge as they approach the eye ; so that the whole bundle of rays from an object is able to enter the eye through the small opening called the pupil, and, traversing the body of the eye, is received on the inner side of the posterior-wall, called the retina. On it the image of the object is formed, exactly similar to the apparent form of the object itself, only greatly reduced in size and reversed in position. In order to understand the explanations which follow, it is important to consider attentively this bundle of converging rays which the eye receives from every object upon which it is turned. Every object seems to be charged with the luminous quality we call light, which is profusely diffused abroad in all directions. Whenever the eye is directed to any object, it receives a shower of these luminous vibrations. It suits our present purpose to regard these vibrations of light as moving in straight lines ; that is, a bundle of lines from an object converging to the eye. The form of the bundle of rays depends upon the form of the object.

Thus, if a square be placed directly in front, so that the eye is equally distant from each of the four corners, it is plain that the rays of light from this square, converging to the eye, will form a true right pyramid, having four sides, with the square for its base, and its apex in the eye as in Fig. 11.

In this case the sides of the pyramid of rays would be bounded by four equal isosceles triangles; and the central ray of light c, from the square, would be the axis of the pyramid of rays. If, now, this pyramid of rays is cut by a plane perpendicular to the axis or central ray, and parallel to the base, the section will be geometrically similar to the base, that is a square. The section will, therefore, be a

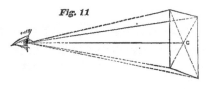

Fig. 11

true picture of the square, and will correspond in form to the little spot in the eye formed by the square.

If the square is turned obliquely to the eye, so that the rays of light are thrown off obliquely to the surface of the square, and a cross-section of the rays is made perpendicular to the central ray, the section will present a true picture of the apparent form of the square in its oblique position; and it will be exactly similar to the image formed in the eye by the rays from the square in its oblique position. There are several ways of making these facts apparent. One method is, by employment of models in a conical or pyramidal form built obliquely on several bases, showing cross-sections. The only objection to this mode of experiment and proof is in the cost of the models, which are difficult of construction.

An easier method is, to set up a plate of glass perpendicular to the central ray, and, looking through it at right angles to its surface upon any object, to trace upon the glass with a common pencil, or one made of soap, the outline of the object, with the head in a fixed position.

The outline on the glass will be a true picture of the object. The glass will be a cross-section of the bundle of rays from the object (Fig. 12).

Thus, the picture of the plane *a b c d* will be accurately traced on

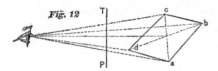

Fig. 12

the transparent plane interposed at T P. Hence, we may state this general principle: *A true picture of an object may be obtained by tracing its apparent form on a transparent plane perpendicular to the central ray from the object, or by a cross-section of the rays from the object perpendicular to the central ray.*

THE DRAWING OF THE RECTANGLE OR OF THE SQUARE.

The drawing of the rectangle or the square presents a few points of special interest, which the student would do well to consider, and to master completely, in order to make the drawing of all rectangles easy and sure.

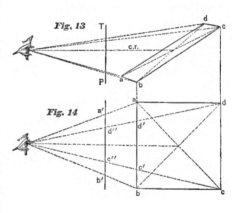

Fig. 13

Fig. 14

First, when two sides, *a b* and *c d* (in this case, the upper and lower sides), of a square or a rectangle are perpendicular to the central ray, but one of them, *d c*, at a greater distance from the eye than the other, as in Fig. 13, then the two lines which are perpendicular to *c. r.,*

i.e., *a b* and *d c*, are seen to be parallel; but, since they are unequally distant from the eye, the nearer line, *a b*, will appear to be
longer than *d c*.

Thus, in Fig. 14, which is the plan of the above, the rays from *c d*
will be seen to cross *a b* at *c′ d′;* so that, relatively to *a b*, *c d* will
appear to be only as long as *c″ d″* on the transparent plane. If we
examine the image formed on T P, we find that it consists of the
following elements : viz., apparent height, 1 to 2
(Fig. 15) ; the apparent length of *c d* is *c″ d″*, and of
a b is *a′ b′;* the apparent length of *a d* is *a′ d″*, and
of *b c*, *b′ c″;* thus, the figure of the rectangle will be
given in the figure *a′ b′ c″ d″*. It will be seen, there-
fore, that the lines *a d* and *b c* will appear to be convergent lines, seem-
ing to approach each other as they recede from the eye. By assuming
four points on any two receding lines, we could construct a rectangle
as above, and proceed in the same method to show the convergence.

In the same way it may be proved that all receding parallel lines,
in whatever position, seem to converge or incline to each other as
they recede, and would, therefore, if extended sufficiently, meet in
the same point. In all
cases this will appear from
the fact that the distance
between them, which is a
line of a certain length,
seems to diminish in length
as it becomes more distant.

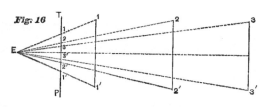

Thus, in Fig. 16 let E represent the position of the eye, and 1, 2, 3,
the positions of three equal lines in the same plane with the eye and

with each other. Let the line 1 1′ be at a certain distance, 2 2′ at twice, and 3 3′ at three times, the distance of 1 1′ from the eye. Draw lines from the extremities of each of these lines to E, and, at their intersection with T P, we shall have their relative apparent lengths. Thus, 2 2′ will appear to be one-half as long as 1 1′, because it is twice the distance from the eye; and 3 3′ will appear to be one-third as long as 1 1′, because it is three times as far from the eye. Hence it follows that the apparent length of a line is inversely proportional to its distance from the eye. If 2 2′ and 3 3′ were moved up to the position of 1 1′, they would appear to be of the same length.

We have thus obtained these additional general principles : viz., *First, Equal magnitudes appear equal at equal distances ; Second, Equal magnitudes appear unequal at unequal distances ; and, Third, Equal magnitudes appear inversely proportional to their distances.*

These principles determine the convergence of all parallel lines as they recede from the eye.

THE APPARENT FORMS OF ANGLES.

Place a square plane in such a position that all the angles are equally distant from the eye, as in Fig. 17, *a b c d*. It is evident, that, in this position, all the angles will appear to be right angles, as they really are; but if the plane is revolved about *c d* into the position *a′ b′ c′ d′*, so as to bring *a b* into the position of *a′ b′*, the appearance will be at once changed, and all the right angles will have been apparently destroyed. Thus, the angles at *a′* and *b′* will appear to have been opened, while those at *c′* and *d* will appear to have been partly closed. If the revolution of the plane about the line *c′ d′* were continued, the process of opening one set and closing the other set would go on until all the angles would appear to be extinguished; the points *a′* and *b′* coming into the same line with the eye, and the whole plane assuming the appearance of a straight line.

Now, since the angles at *a′* and *b′* in the oblique position appear to be opened more than right angles, and since rays from the angle *a′* are more oblique than at *b′*, and since the angles at *c′* and *d′* appear partly closed, considering what was shown on p. 30 we may deduce the following general statements : —

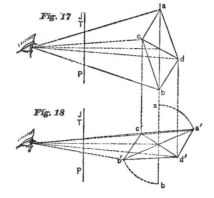

Whenever a rectangular plane is seen obliquely, the nearest and the farthest angles appear obtuse, the latter being the more obtuse ; and the two intermediate angles appear always acute.

This rule will apply to every possible position of the rectangle and of the square, which is only a particular case of the rectangle. As rectangular (solids) volumes are drawn by representing their separate faces, and as each face must be solved or read by itself, as well as with reference to the others, the principles above stated go far to enable the student to represent accurately rectangular solids.

There is, however, one other deduction which may be noticed. If we have three rectangular planes in an oblique position, as, for instance, the three sides of a cube forming one solid angle, there will appear to be three obtuse angles about that point. This will always

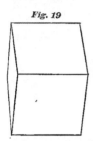

Fig. 19

be the case when three sides are visible : there can never be a combination of one right and two obtuse angles, or of one acute and two obtuse angles ; *but the* three angles about that nearest point of the cube must always be obtuse, as in Fig. 19.

The advantage of this rule will be appreciated by every teacher, as it offers at once a test for many doubtful points where the eye alone might not be able to detect the error.

THE DRAWING OF THE CUBE.

Definition : The *CUBE* is a volume bounded by six equal squares. First, place the cube on a horizontal plane directly in front, with the two side-lines of the front square equally distant from the eye ; the top of the square being a little nearer than the bottom, so that only the front and the top of the cube will be seen (Fig. 20). In this position the front face of the cube is usually drawn as a square, with the side-lines vertical, for the same reason that we should draw the sides of a house vertical, and not converging as they recede upward. We should then ascertain by observation, on the pencil held at arm's length in a vertical position, corresponding with $a\,c$, the measurement of the apparent height of the

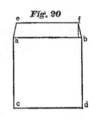

Fig. 20

upper face of the cube. Let us suppose it to be one-fourth as high as the front face. Divide one vertical side of the front face into four equal parts, and place one of these parts above the line $a\,b$, and draw *e f* of indefinite length, parallel to *a b*. Next observe how much shorter *e f* appears to be than *a b*, and mark its apparent length on *a b*, and draw dotted vertical lines from these points to *e* and *f:* the lines *a e* and *b f* may now be drawn, and the figure is complete.

Next place the cube so that three sides will be visible; the model still resting on a horizontal plane, showing the front, right side, and top (Fig. 21).

The first line to be drawn is the nearest vertical, *a b*. This line is the measure of every other line. The second line, *a c*, must be placed by observing its position in the model, its degree of inclination to an imaginary horizontal line through *a*, and its length compared with the standard line *a b*.

Fig. 21

Then the third line, *a f*, should be read from the model, as to position, inclination, and length, in a similar manner. We have now one line in each of the three sets of parallels to be drawn.

Since every other line in the model is parallel to one of these three, therefore the three lines are the ruling lines of the drawing. We should next observe if *c d* is shorter than *a b*, and, if so, how much, representing it in its true proportion: then draw *b d*. Compare *f e* with *a b*, and draw it. Connect *b* with *e*. By drawing *b d* and *b e*, the convergence of the lines *f g* and *c g* has been determined; so that it is only necessary that they should have the same degree of convergence, as the lines are respectively parallel to each. These lines complete the drawing of the model. If correctly drawn, there will be, first, three obtuse angles about the point *a ;* second, the angles at *d*, *g*, and *e* will also appear obtuse, and more obtuse than the angles in their respective planes at *a ;* third, the remaining angles will be acute.

The third position of the cube is one in which the three faces will appear about equal.   Place the cube on an inclined plane, or put something under the back corner, so that there will be no vertical lines in the model.

In this position let *a* be the nearest point : draw first the line *a b*, which seems to be nearest vertical ; then the line *a c* to the left ; and third, *a d*, comparing the last two lines with the first to obtain their

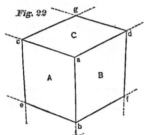

different lengths (Fig. 22).   Having obtained the positions and lengths of these three lines, it only remains to draw the other six lines with the proper convergence, which must be noted from the model itself. There will be, when complete, three sets of lines ; each set converging to a different point.

Let us observe, again, that about the point *a* we have three obtuse angles, and that the opposite angle on each face is more obtuse than the angle in the same plane at *a*, and that the angles at *c*, *d*, and *b* are all acute.   There is one other rule very useful in the criticism of drawings by pupils deducible from this case ; viz., Take the two faces A and B, and call *c e*, *d f*, and *a b* the side-lines of the two faces, *a b* being the dividing line : then these side-lines will converge in a direction opposite to the other face C ; i.e., downwards.   Now take the two faces C and B, with the dividing line *a d*, and with the side-lines *b f* and *c g*.   They will converge in a direction opposite to the other face A ; i.e., to the right.

In the same way the side-lines of the two faces A and C, i.e., *a c,* *b e,* and *d g,* will converge in a direction opposite to the other face B ; i.e., to the left.   Hence the rule : *In drawing any rectangular solid, three faces being visible, the side-lines of any two faces will seem to converge in a direction opposite to the third visible face.*   It will be seen that the third visible face always indicates the ends of the lines nearest the eye.

THE METHOD OF DRAWING THE HEXAGON AND THE HEXAGONAL PRISM.

In drawing the hexagon and the hexagonal prism and the pyramid, we have first to consider the elements of the hexagon as a geometrical quantity.   Describe a circle, and, with the radius from each end of the horizontal diameter as a center, cut the circumference in points above and below.   By this means the circumference is divided into six equal arcs : drawing the chords of these arcs, we complete the figure of the hexagon (Fig. 23).   Draw radial lines from the outer angles to the center, thus dividing the hex-

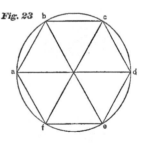

Fig. 23

agon into six equal equilateral triangles, all having their inner angles at the center of the hexagon (Fig. 24).   If we draw the altitudes of the two triangles having the common base *a o,* we shall have the line *b f,* dividing the base *a o* into two equal parts ; for it is evident that the altitude of an equilateral triangle will always bisect the base.   Again, if the altitudes of the two triangles having the common base *o d* are drawn, we shall have the line *c e,* dividing the base *o d* into two equal parts.   Since *a o* and *o d* are equal, it is plain that the diameter is divided into four equal parts, which we will number 1, 2, 3, 4, beginning at the left.

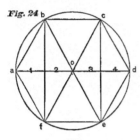

Fig. 24

Let us now turn the hexagon into a position oblique to the eye, so that the point *a* will be nearer to the eye than the point *d :* it will be seen that the points *c* and *e* will appear nearer to each other than *b* and *f,* because the line *b f* is nearer to the eye than *c e* (Fig. 25). Hence the two lines *b c* and *f e,* which are parallel to *a d,* will appear to converge : also, the four geometrically equal parts of the diameter, being at unequal distances from the eye, will appear unequal ; the nearest part, 1, will appear to be the longest ; and 2, the next in length ; 3, the next ; and 4 the shortest of all. Again, let us suppose we have the hexagonal prism before us, with one end visible in an oblique position. We first read from the model the central rectangle *b c e f ;* that is, we observe these four lines, and draw them in their

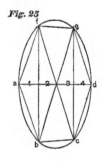

Fig. 25

relative positions and relations. Thus, as *b c* and *f e* converge upwards, supposing the eye to be a little above the model, we have the central rectangle *b c e f* drawn in its true position (Fig. 26). Draw the diagonals *b e* and *c f :* they will cross each other in O, the true center of the rectangle. Now draw the diameter through O, parallel to the two lines *b c* and *f e ;* that is, so that it will converge at the same point with them. We find that we have the two

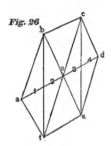

Fig. 26

central divisions of the diameter, 2 and 3, represented in their proportional lengths ; and 2 will appear to be longer than 3. Comparing
these two divisions, we have the ratio between the several divisions of
the diameter; for, by as much as 2 appears to be longer than 3, by
exactly the same proportion will 1 appear to be longer than 2, and 3
than 4 : so that we can point off the first and the last divisions of the
diameter by observing the ratio of the two middle divisions. Having
thus placed the points *a d* on the diameter, we have only to draw the
adjacent sides to complete the apparent form of the hexagon in this
position.

It will be seen, that, to draw the hexagon from the model, it is
only necessary to read and draw the central rectangle ; and all the
rest follows necessarily, without any further examination of the
model : and, provided these four lines of this rectangle are correctly
located, the whole hexagon is easily represented in its true proportions.

Any two opposite sides may be taken for the ends of the rectangle,
but it is usually best to choose the upper and the lower (when there
is an upper and a lower). The four lines must be drawn with great
care, allowing no error of observation or of execution to occur ; since
the rest of the hexagon depends upon them.

This analysis covers every conceivable
position of the hexagon. Let us suppose
that one of the possible positions of the central rectangle is represented by the figure
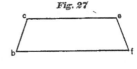
Fig. 27

b c e f, b f and *c e* being the longer lines (Fig. 27). Draw the diagonals
cutting each other at *o,* the center of the rectangle. Through this
point draw the diameter as before, parallel to the ends *b c* and *f e.*

We shall then have the two central divisions 2 and 3, giving the ratio (Fig. 28). Laying off the points *a* and *d*, on the diameter, so as to

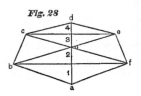

Fig. 28

give the four divisions of the diameter in their diminishing ratio from 1 to 4, draw the other four lines *a b*, *c d*, *a f*, and *d e*, and the hexagon is completed.

In the same way, if we have the central rectangle in the position *b c e f*, draw the diagonals to ascertain the central point *o* (Fig. 29); and through *o* draw the diameter as before, parallel to the lines *f e* and *b c*, which, in this case, have but slight convergence: next, lay off the points *a* and *d*, as before, and then complete the hexagon *a b c d e f*.

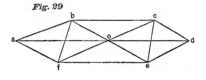

Fig. 29

These several positions may be regarded as typical, all others being referable to the same.

Fig. 30

Let us now suppose we have before us the hexagonal prism standing on one of its bases, the upper base being visible: we should draw the nearest line of that visible base *a b* (Fig. 30). Next, by observation, determine the position of *a c*, the nearest side of the central rectangle, and compare its length with *a b* (in this case, it is two-thirds of *a b*). Determine *b d* in the same way, and draw *c d* and the diagonals: through the center *o* draw the diameter parallel to *a b* and *c d*. Now, since *g o* is longer than *o n*, make *e g* longer than *g o* by the same ratio, and *n f* shorter than *o n* by the same ratio, and complete the hexagon. Draw the vertical lines of the prism.

Make *j h* parallel to *a b*; *h i* converging with *b f*, *c e*, and *a d*, *j k* with *a e*
and *f d*. The amount of convergence
is to be determined by observation.

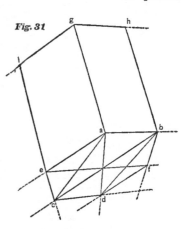

Fig. 31

Let us next suppose the hexagonal
prism placed in a position oblique to
the eye, and inclined; *a b* representing
the nearest line of the central rectangle of the visible base (Fig. 31):
observe and draw the two side-lines of
the same rectangle, *a c* and *b d*, and
join *c d;* drawing the diagonals, we
find the center, through which, as before, draw the diameter parallel to the lines *a b* and *c d*.
We fix the points *e* and *f* in
due proportion from the two
central divisions of the same
line, and complete the hexagon.

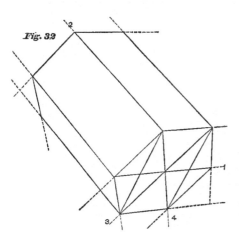

Fig. 32

Observing the inclination of
the side-lines of the prism, draw
them in the correct position
with the proper convergence.
Next, draw the visible lines of
the invisible base, converging
with their respective parallels
of the visible base, *g h* with *a b*,
g i with *a e*. It will be seen that there will be four systems of con-

verging lines, and that *a b* may be taken for the initial line of the first system, *a g* of the second, the diagonal *b c* of the third, and the diagonal *a d* of the fourth. A fifth system would be indicated by *a c* and *b d*, but it is not essential. Following the method here indicated, the hexagon is an easy subject to draw in all possible positions (Fig. 32).

THE CIRCLE.

A circle seen in various positions, in whole or in part, appears to the eye as a circle, a straight line, an ellipse, a parabola, or as a hyperbola; that is, mathematically speaking, as one of the conic sections.

First, A circle is seen as a true circle when the central ray of light from the plane of the circle is perpendicular to that plane; that is,

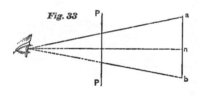

Fig. 33

when it forms a right angle above and below, and to the right and left, with the plane. Thus, let *a b* represent the side view of a circle (Fig. 33), and the central ray of light from *n* form a right angle on all sides with the plane of the circle. Then the circle will *appear* as a true circle; for if we cut the rays of light which come in the form of a cone, from the circle to the eye, by a plane at *p p*, perpendicular to the central ray, we shall have a section of the cone of rays parallel to the base of the cone, consequently a sub-section, and therefore similar to the base, that is a circle.

Second, A circle is seen as a straight line when the rays of light proceeding from the circle to the eye move in the direction of the plane of the circle. Let *a b* and *a' b'*, Fig. 34 and Fig. 35, represent the side view of a circle, with the eye placed in the direction of the plane of the circle. Then the circle would appear as a straight line. In the upper figure the circle is in a vertical, and in the lower figure in a horizontal, position. The rays from the circle to the eye will be in a single plane : no part of the upper or under surface, or right or left surface, gives rays to the eye. Hence, a section of the plane of rays at P P and P′P′ would be a straight line ; that is, the circle, thus seen, would have the appearance of a straight line.

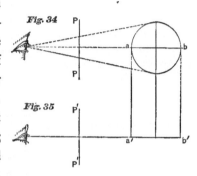

Third, A circle is seen as an ellipse when the ray of light proceeds obliquely from the plane to the eye. Thus, let *a b* represent a side view of a circle with the eye at E, and the central ray oblique to the plane of the circle (Fig. 36). Then the figure of the circle, on the plane of section, P P, will appear as a true ellipse. The proof of this theorem will be better illustrated farther on ; but a real ocular demonstration may be had by constructing of wood an oblique cone on a circular base, making a cross-section corresponding to P P. We may note here, however, that, as the obliquity of the central ray with the plane of the circle increases, the diameter, more oblique to this ray, becomes

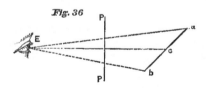

the more foreshortened, and that the one which remains at right angles to this ray will not be foreshortened at all. Hence, since these two diameters are at right angles to each other, it will be evi-

dent, that apparently the circle becomes flattened in the direction of
one of its diameters, as in Fig. 37 A A, the diameter in the vertical
plane of the eye, *a a*, the same when revolved into its oblique position
to the central ray E *c*. The inter-

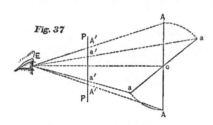

section of the rays from each, on
the plane P P, shows their relative
apparent lengths A' A' without
foreshortening, and *a' a'*, in its
oblique position, foreshortened.
We may learn still further, by the
examination of a cone, from which a section of the ellipse is made,
that the perimeter of the ellipse, in its oblique position to the central
ray, may be made to appear to cover and coincide exactly with the
circumference of the circle at right angles to the central ray.

Fig. 38. Let E *a b* be a cone, and *m n* the section. It is a true
ellipse. Place the eye at E : the contour of the ellipse will appear
to fall against the circumference of the circle, because the rays of

light from the latter will pass directly through the former ; hence
they will appear to coincide. Now,
if an ellipse, in an oblique position,
may be made to coincide with a circle in a perpendicular position, it
is reasonable to suppose that a cir-

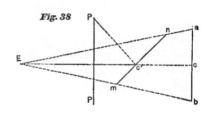

cle in a position oblique to the central ray may be made to coincide with
the outline of an ellipse at right angles to the central ray. In Fig. 38
the ellipse seen from the direction of P appears as a perfect ellipse.
While seen from the apex of the cone *e*, it appears as a perfect circle.

That the figure of the circle in a position oblique to the central ray will appear to be a true and symmetrical ellipse is, moreover, evident from the following diagrams.

In order fully to appreciate the nice conditions and relations of the apparent ellipse to the *parent* circle, and several points of great interest in all subsequent practice shown by these and following diagrams, careful study and attention to every particular is demanded of the student.

Figs. 39 and 40 represent the circle in nearly the same position with reference to the eye.

The first, Fig. 39, is the plan of the circle, with the eye in the same horizontal plane as the circle. It shows the place of the apparent diameter at $a'b'$ to the left, and nearer to the eye than the real diameter: the place of the apparent diameter $a'b'$ is found by locating the tangential rays a' E, b' E; these are drawn by bisecting the line E c, c being the center of the circle: taking the central point thus found, as a center, with the half-length of the line as a radius, describe the arc $a'c b'$; it will give the points $a'b'$ on the circumference, from which tangential rays may be drawn to the eye. The line $a'b'$ must be the apparent diameter, because it subtends a larger visual angle than any other line that can be drawn in the circle.

The second, Fig. 40, is a vertical projection of the same circle, revolved a little so as to come into a position slightly oblique to the eye, as indicated by the diameter $m'n'$: m' has been moved downward from m, its position in Fig. 39, and n' upward from n.

In this position the upper face of the circle sends its rays to the eye, and its image is formed on the retina. Now we wish to ascertain whether that portion of the circle to the left of $a'b'$ appears to be just as wide as the larger part, to the right of that line, or whether that part of the diameter *m′ b′* subtends as large an angle as the part *b′ n′*: this may be easily determined by bisecting in the usual way the angle *m′* E *n′*, the whole visual angle subtended by the diameter, and through the bisecting point 3 draw a line from the eye to the diameter

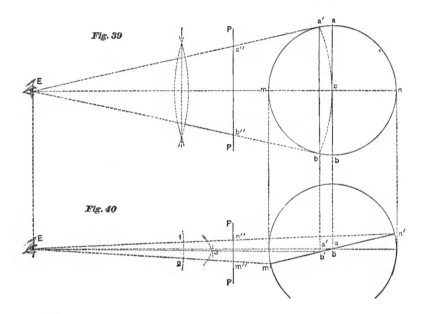

Fig. 39

Fig. 40

m′ n′, cutting it in the point *b′*, the place of the apparent diameter in Fig. 39. It seems, therefore, that the smaller part of the circle to the left of the line *a′ b′* appears to be just as large as the larger part of the circle to the right of *a′ b′*, and that the apparent form of the circle in this position is an ellipse, with *a′ b′* for its longer diameter, dividing the ellipse into two equal parts. We may say here, that there is in the illustration a slight error, which will be noticed farther on, but which does not, in this case, vitiate the conclusions very much.

Taking the two lines *a" b"* and *n" m"* on the P P, the plane of section, as the longer and the shorter diameter of an ellipse, we shall obtain very nearly the apparent form of the circle, as seen in Fig. 41. Thus we have the true figure of the apparent form of the circle in this position, and by the same means we

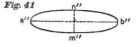

can obtain its apparent form in all positions intermediate between that in Fig. 39 and a position at right angles to the central ray.

A true picture of the circle, when seen obliquely, according to the definition of a true picture given on p. 32, can only be obtained by cutting the cone of rays from the circle to the eye by a plane perpendicular to the central ray or axis of the cone of rays. Although other sections than this may give ellipses, yet they will not possess the proportions of the true picture (Fig. 42). Let A B be the vertical projection of the circle at an angle of 45° to a line drawn from the apparent center

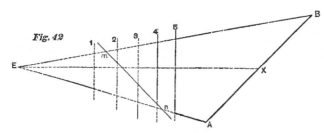

of the circle to E, the position of the eye: then the oblique cone of rays will be formed upon the circular base A B. Now, all sections, as 1, 2, 3, 4, 5, perpendicular to the axis, will present true pictures of the circle: but, if we take an oblique section of the cone of rays *m n* perpendicular to the plane of the circle A B, it is quite evident that the section can not present a true picture of the circle A B; because the section itself will be a circle.

Drawing the section *m n* (Fig. 43) at right angles to the base A B, and then revolving the part of the cone E *m n* about the axis E *x*, through 180°, it is plain that the point *m* will be revolved into the

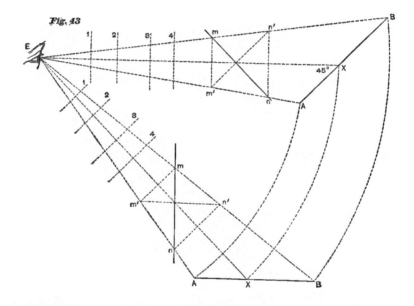

Fig. 43

position *m'*, and the point *n* into the position *n'*, and the line *m n* will be found in the position *m' n'*, parallel to the base A B. Thus, the section *m' n'* will be a section parallel to the base A B, and geometrically similar: therefore it will be a circle.

The revolution of the plane of section, which is at right angles to the base, through 180°, brings it into a position parallel to the same base, and shows at once that it must be a circle; as all sections of a cone parallel to the base must be similar to the base, and consequently circles.

It will not alter the conditions, nor invalidate the conclusions at all, to revolve the whole diagram about the point E, through an angle of 45°, so that the base, A B, will be brought into a horizontal position, and the plane of section *m n* into a vertical position: the section *m n* in the vertical position will still be a true circle; and it follows, of course, that it can not be a picture of the circle A B. It may, therefore, be asserted that a true picture of the circle in this oblique position will be found by a section at right angles to the central ray of the cone of rays, and that all other sections, not at right angles to that ray, will differ, more or less, from the true picture, according to their obliquity to this central ray.

The slight error in the illustration on p. 48, which results from the change of position in the place of the apparent diameter in Fig. 40, the circle being slightly turned into an oblique position, can now be corrected if desired. This change of position of the apparent diameter, and the method by which we may ascertain the true position of the apparent diameter of the circle, when it is at any particular angle of obliquity to the central ray, may be understood by reference to Fig. 44.

In Fig. 44 we have the vertical projection, *m' n'*, of the circle in a horizontal position; the eye being at E': in the lower figure we have the plan of the circle *m n*, the eye being at E. With the eye in this position with reference to the circle, we have already seen that the apparent diameter will be at *a' b'*. Now, if the eye is revolved through an arc of 90° to the position E" immediately over the center of the cir-

cle, it will be evident, that, in this position, the apparent diameter can
no longer be at $a'\,b'$, but that the apparent and the real diameters
will occupy one and the same place, and will be identical.   If we move
the eye from E″ back along the arc of 90° towards its former position,

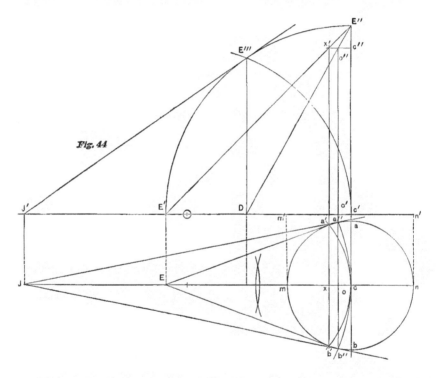

Fig. 44

it is evident that the position of the apparent diameter will recede
from the position of the real diameter until it reaches the position
$a'\,b'$, when the eye has returned to the position E′, thus passing over
the entire space between $a\,b$ and $a'\,b'$.   Let us now see if we can

determine the position of the apparent diameter when the eye is at any particular point on this arc.

In the passage of the eye over the arc from E' to E'', it moves vertically over every point of the radial line E' c' ; and, when it has passed vertically over every point of the radial line E' c', the apparent diameter of the circle has receded from its extreme position a' b' to the position of the real diameter a b. Hence it follows, that, when the eye has passed vertically over any particular portion of the line E' c', the apparent diameter will have passed over the same proportion of the line x c, the difference between the extreme position of the apparent diameter and the real diameter in the plan.* We may, therefore, find the position of the apparent diameter with the eye at any given point E''' in the arc E' E'' by drawing to E' c' a vertical line from E''', the assumed position of the eye on the arc E' E'', to D. This line will divide the line E' c' into two parts, E'D and D c'. Then, by dividing the line x c into similar proportional parts, we can determine the position of the apparent diameter with the eye at the given point.

To divide x c into proportionals similar to the divisions of E' c', draw a line from E' to E'', produce b' a' so as to cut E' E'' in x', and make x' c'' equal and parallel to x c. From D, the point of division on E' c', draw a line to E'' cutting x' c'' proportionally to E' c' in the point o''. (See "Robinson's Geometry," Bk. 2, Theo. 17, *et seq.*)

By drawing a parallel to E'' c' from o'' cutting x c in o, we shall have the point in x c through which we can draw a'' b'', the apparent diameter of the circle m' n' or m n, with the eye at the point E'''.

This method is true for all other positions of the eye on the arc

* This method of determining the apparent diameter is given, without entering upon trigonometric principles,

E′ E″, since E‴ is any point in it. Hence, by combining this method with one on p. 48, all error, however slight, may be eliminated from that problem.

The correctness of the foregoing solution may be tested also in another way. It is evident, when the eye is at E E′, that if two planes are drawn through the eye, and tangent to the circle on opposite sides, and perpendicular to the plane of the circle, the planes will cut each other in a vertical line passing through the eye, and will be tangent to the circle at the extremities of the apparent diameter *a′ b′;* as the tangent lines E *b′* and E *a′* would be the traces of these planes, and a vertical line drawn through E would be the line of their intersection. It is also evident, that, when the eye is at E″, these two planes would be tangent to the circle at the extremities of the real diameter *a b*, and that their intersection would be in a horizontal line passing through E″. Now, at any intermediate points along the arc E′ E″, the intersection of these two planes, if extended, would cut the plane of the circle extended. Thus, draw through the point E‴ a line tangent to the arc E′ E″, and extend the line until it cuts the line *c′* E′ extended in J′: this will be the trace of the line of intersection of the two planes passing through the eye at E‴, and tangent to the circle at the extremities of the apparent diameter *a″ b″*. For if we project the point J′ on to the horizontal plane at J, and then draw from J tangents to the circle, by bisecting the line J *c*, and drawing an arc from its central point with the half-length of the line as a radius, cutting the circumference, the arc will pass through the two points *a″ b″*, the extremities of the apparent diameter, thus showing that the two planes drawn tangent to the circle, and intersecting at the eye in a line tangent to the arc E′ E″, at the point E‴, the place of the eye, will also be tangent to the circle at the extremities of the apparent diameter[1] *d″ b″*.

Fourth, A. When a part only of a circle from a point somewhere

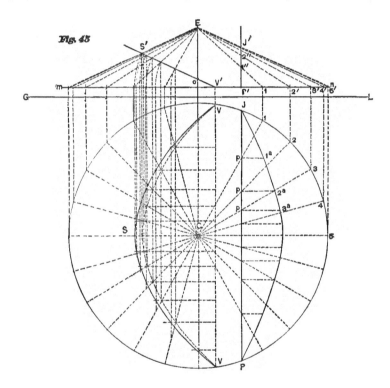

Fig. 45

in a straight line drawn perpendicular to the plane of the circle at its center is seen through a plane parallel to this line (Fig. 45). Let *m n* be a vertical projection of the circle with the eye at E, over the center *c′*. Then we have a cone of rays on a circle as a base, with E as

the apex.   Cut this cone by a plane, J′ P′ parallel to the axis of the cone.
The rays from the circumference of the circle on this plane will trace
its true curve, as seen from the point E.   The section will be a true
hyperbola, since from geometry we learn that all sections of a cone
parallel to the axis will be hyperbolas.   The true form of the curve
is projected on the horizontal plane between the points J P on the
straight line J P as a base.   The elements of the curve are obtained
by laying off on J P from the points *p p p* and the vertical distances
P′ 1″, P′ 2″, etc., each on its respective radial lines C 1, C 2, C 3, etc.

B.   When a part of a circle is seen through a plane S′ V′ parallel
to E *n*, *m n* being the circle as before, then that part of the circle traced
upon the plane S′ V′, as seen from E, will present the form of the
parabola, because it is a section of the cone of rays parallel to one
side of the cone.   From geometry we know that all such sections are
parabolas.   The development of the curve in its true form is seen in
the full line V S V ; while the dotted curved line between V and V just
to the left of V S V is the horizontal projection of the curve of section,
and not its true form.   The curve V S V is obtained by throwing down
from S′ V′ all the elements or normals of the curve from V′ as a center
upon the horizontal *m n*, and then projecting them upon the horizontal
plane, each upon its own normal drawn from V V.

All possible forms of the circle as seen in various positions are
referable to some one of the conic sections, all consequently taking
their places among the absolute mathematical figures.   Let the student
thoroughly master these forms, and trust to no methods not referable
to fixed geometric formulas.

METHOD OF DRAWING CIRCULAR OBJECTS.

The application of the principles already developed relating to the circle will be found necessary whenever the student attempts to draw any circular object, or objects having circular bases, such as the cylinder, cone, frustum of a cone, vases, cups, saucers, wheels, and a great multitude of objects. But, in order to deal successfully with many of them, it will be necessary to consider several other facts and principles, as applied to combinations of circles. Let us take first the cylinder, as one of the simplest volumes, having two circular bases.

There are eight rules applicable to the dimensions and positions of the cylinder. As the same rules apply with some slight modifications to all objects having two opposite circular bases, as vases, goblets, etc., they are in an eminent degree generic, and consequently important. We will now consider several facts relating to the cylinder, and see what deductions we can draw from them.

First, When the two bases of a cylinder are equally distant from the eye, both are invisible (Fig. 46).

Fig. 46

An apparent exception to this rule would be found by taking a cylinder of the dimensions of a silver dollar. Placing it so as to be seen by both eyes, both bases would be visible, the one to one eye, and the opposite to the other ; but the rule requires that we should look with one eye only, in which case the exception vanishes.

Second, The visible base of a cylinder is always nearer to the eye than the invisible base.

Third, The visible base is always apparently longer than the invisible base.

Fourth, The invisible base is always wider in proportion to its length than the visible base.

The last two rules may be stated thus : *The visible base is always longer and narrower, and the invisible base is always shorter and proportionately wider.*

Fifth, The longer diameters of the ellipses, which represent the bases of a cylinder, are always perpendicular to the axis of the cylinder.

Sixth, The shorter diameters of the ellipses are always coincident with the axis of the cylinder.

Seventh, The side-lines of a cylinder always appear to converge in the direction of the invisible base.

Eighth, When a cylinder is in a vertical position, the plane of delineation is supposed to be vertical also ; and the side-lines are drawn vertical and parallel, and of course without convergence, in accordance with the general practice in all architectural subjects.

In illustration of this last statement, reference may be made to Geometrical Perspective, *where all regular polygons which are parallel to the picture plane are represented, in the picture, by regular polygons.* In all architectural subjects, the plane of delineation is always supposed to be vertical.

To illustrate the third rule, that the ellipse representing the visible base of a cylinder is always longer than the ellipse representing the invisible base, we have only to consider that the diameter of the cylinder is a constant quantity, and therefore the same at either end. If it is the same constant quantity at unequal distances from the eye, the nearer end must appear the longer (see illustration on p. 33), as in Fig. 47. Let *a c* represent the axis of a cylinder, *b d* the nearer, and *e f* the farther diameter: then *b d* will be longer than *e f,* because a nearer line appears longer than an equal line more distant.

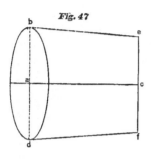

Fig. 47

The rule that the invisible base is always wider in proportion to its length than the visible base, will be readily understood by observing the following diagram, Fig. 48, where E represents the position of the eye, and *a e, b f, c g,* and *d h,* four equal and parallel circles; the lines *a e, b f,* etc., showing the actual width from front to back. By drawing rays from each of these circles to the eye, it is evident that the circle *a e* will have no apparent width, because it is in the same plane as the eye; and consequently it appears as a straight line: the circle *b f* will have some apparent width; while *c g* will appear still wider, and *d h* widest of all. For, if we interpose the transparent plane T P, the relative apparent width of the several circles will be expressed by the distances *b' f', c' g',* and *d' h',* of which

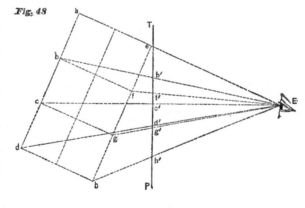

Fig. 48

d' h' is nearly twice as long as *b' f' ;* and *d h,* of which *d' h'* is the apparent width, is the most distant from the eye: hence the rule.

It will be seen from the diagram that the rays of light come more directly from the surface of the circle *d h* than from either of the others. The same holds good for every invisible base of a cylinder as compared with the visible base in any possible position. The rule, that the longer diameters of the ellipses are always perpendicular to the axis, may be made clear to the pupil by walking around a circle

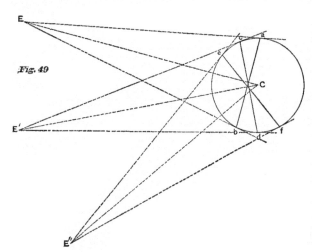

Fig. 49

and observing its greatest apparent length. Let C be the center of the circle, and E E′ E″, Fig. 49, represent the successive positions of the eye : the longer diameters or major axes of the ellipses will join the tangential rays ; i.e., from E the longer diameter will be at *a b*, from E′ the longer diameter will be at *c d*, from E″, at *e f:* and in each case the apparent axis of the cylinder of which this circle is the base will appear to be perpendicular to these diameters at their central points, because it is perpendicular to the plane in which they are. This is a matter that should be determined by observation, by walking round the circle and noticing how the apparent diameter seems to follow, keeping its position perpendicular to the central ray. And so it will be for all possible positions in which the cylinder may be placed.

The sixth rule, that the shorter diameters are coincident with the apparent axis of the cylinder, may be readily understood from the fact, that, if the longer diameter is perpendicular to the axis, the shorter must be coincident with the axis, because it is perpendicular to the longer diameter. The truth of the proposition should be confirmed by observing the cylinder in various positions.

That the side-lines of a cylinder will always appear to converge in the direction of the invisible base, is evident from the fact, that, the apparent diameters of the cylinder being geometrically equal, the more distant will appear the shorter: hence, as we have seen, the invisible base is apparently shorter; and the lines connecting the extremities of the two bases will appear to converge in the direction of the invisible base.

The eighth rule, in regard to harmonizing the fundamental principles of model-drawing with architectural methods, where all vertical lines are drawn vertical in the picture: we call attention to the fact, that the principles already laid down have no reference to merely vertical or horizontal positions, but simply relate to absolute relations of the object to the eye in *all possible* positions, with the plane of section of the rays, that is, the plane of perspective, perpendicular to the central ray of light.

In architectural methods the plane of section is supposed to be parallel to the vertical lines in the object; and, of course, the central ray would be supposed to be horizontal. This would not always be *really* the case. This point presents no difficulty to the student who makes himself thoroughly acquainted with the principles here deduced.

It should be observed here, that the differences in the lengths or breadths of the two bases of a cylinder are inversely proportional to the distance of the eye: thus, if the eye is at an infinite distance, there would be no apparent difference in the length and breadth of the ellipses representing the bases, because the rays of light would be practically parallel. So, when the distance is great, the difference is little ; and, when the distance is little, the difference is great. The same principle, for the same general reasons, will be observed in regard to the convergence of lines.

It follows, from the above statement of fact, that every drawing of models, and every picture, can be best seen from one particular point, and will appear accurate from no other point of view. Hence it follows, as a matter of necessity, that the spectator, at the proper distance from the drawing, should place his eye at the point from which all the lines can be seen in their true proportion.

Having deduced our principles and rules, let us now place the cylinder in a vertical position, with the upper base visible. First draw the apparent axis, or, as we may call it, "*the axis;*"

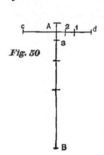

Fig. 50

it always being understood that we do not mean the real axis of the cylinder. In this case the axis A B, Fig. 50, is drawn in a vertical position of any length desired. Compare the length of the upper base with the height of the cylinder. Let us suppose it to be one-half of the axis. Divide the axis A B into two equal parts, and the upper half similarly, and on either side of A measure off horizontally a quarter-length thus obtained, on a line perpendicular to A B. Next compare the apparent width of the ellipse with its length : suppose, in this case, it is found to be four times as long as it is wide. Divide, therefore, one-half of *c d* into two equal parts by a dot at 1, and the quarter of *c d* into halves by a dot at 2. Place this eighth above and below the middle point of the line *c d*, the two eighths making the quarter required (Fig. 51). Thus we have the length of the shorter diameter of the ellipse, as well as its position. It only remains to draw the curve.

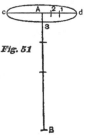

Fig. 51

The lower ellipse should be found in the same way; observing, however, that it must be wider in proportion to its length (which, in this case, is the same as that of the upper) than the upper ellipse (see Rule 8). Thus, if the width of the upper ellipse is one-fourth of its length, the width of the lower ellipse must be

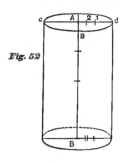

Fig. 52

more than one-fourth of its length. The whole of the lower ellipse should be indicated, the farther half by a dotted or shadowed line only (Fig. 52). Finally the side-lines may be drawn as tangents to the two ellipses, thus completing the drawing of the model.

If, now, the cylinder is placed on its side, so that it appears in an oblique position, we must first observe the apparent position of the axis, comparing its direction with the horizontal, with which we will suppose it to make an angle of 20° (Fig. 53). Draw, as the axis in this position, the line *a b* of any length : observe how long the nearer ellipse is in comparison with the axis. To do this, hold the pencil at arm's length at right angles to a line drawn from the eye to the center of the cylinder, perpendicular to its axis, so that it corresponds to the longer

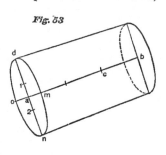

Fig. 53

diameter of the ellipse, and determine its length by moving the thumb along on the side of the pencil towards the end.   Having thus obtained the apparent length of the nearest ellipse, turn the hand, keeping the pencil at right angles to the central ray till it coincides with the axis of the cylinder, with which compare the length of the ellipse.   We will suppose it to be two-thirds of the axis.   Place the point c to mark this : then ac is the length of the longer diameter of the ellipse.   Divide ac into two equal parts, and, drawing a line perpendicular to ab, at a mark off the points d and n respectively above and below a, each at a distance equal to the half of ac. Proceed to find, by means of the pencil as before, the shorter diameter. Suppose it to be one-third of the longer diameter.   Divide, therefore, dn into three equal parts by points 1 and 2.   Since the shorter diameter coincides with the axis of the cylinder, produce the axis, upon which mark the points o and m, each half a third from a.   This gives the position and the length of the shorter diameter.   Then draw the curve of the ellipse through the four points $d\,m\,n\,o$.

Next ascertain the length of the invisible ellipse ; it must be less than that of the visible : measurement with the pencil as before will so determine it.   Do not guess at it.   Put aside guess-work until thorough knowledge is obtained.   Make it as much shorter as it seems to be, and then proceed to estimate the shorter diameter of the same by observing the half-ellipse which is visible.   When these points have been determined, complete the ellipse, drawing the whole curve, the invisible half with a dotted line.   Lastly complete the figure of the cylinder in its oblique position by drawing the sides tangent to the ellipses.

The foregoing explanations and principles will enable the student attentive to them to draw the cylinder in any possible position it may be placed. Let no accident of position or relation trick you out of your knowledge of principles and facts.

There are many necessary modifications of the above principles when we come to draw vases. The same general laws prevail, but they are modified in their application.

For instance, the bases may not have the same actual diameters as in the case of the cylinder. The same law, however, as to position and magnitude exists.

Fig. 54

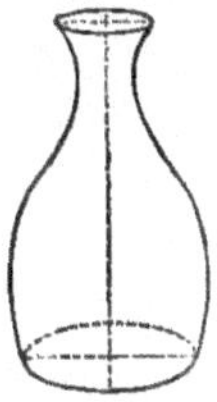

Thus, if the bases, or the circles at the top and bottom of a vase, are unequal, the lower being the larger, still the rule applies ; and the invisible will appear *proportionately* shorter and proportionately wider than the visible base (Fig. 54). The same principle will also hold good for all the minor bands of ornament, if such there are. Thus, as you move in the direction of the invisible base, all ellipses must appear proportionately shorter and wider ; and this is true whether they are *actually* larger or smaller ellipses than the visible one.

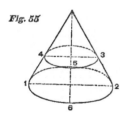

Fig. 55

Other applications of this law are found in drawing the cone, and some bands on vases.

Take the case of two parallel circles, sections of a ·cone. It is evident that the ellipse 4 3, representing the upper circle in Fig. 55, will be proportionately longer and narrower than the lower ellipse, 1 2, according to the rule ; because, if the top of the cone were removed, it would be the visible one. Now, from the nature of the cone, we may be able to see more than half of the curve of the ellipse if the eye is considerably above its plane; as in Fig. 56 we see all of the surface of the cone in front of the line 1 2, which joins the points where the lines to the apex are tangent to the ellipse, and also much more than half of the curve of the ellipse. So when we have two parallel ellipses, as in Fig. 57, we may find that we see more than half the ellipses. It is possible that the width of the band may appear to be greater at the sides than in front, on account of the obliquity of the surface of the band at the

front or middle point tending to foreshorten its width at that point; while the width at the sides will not appear to be foreshortened at all.

Take, again, the rim of a bowl, as Fig. 58. The width of the rim may appear greatest at the sides, nothing at the back, and intermediate at the front, or as wide or wider at the front according to the angle of obliquity, if it happens to be a portion of the surface of a cone with its apex at *a*.

Quite an opposite modification would occur in the case of a surface-band on the sides of a vase or bowl seen below the eye, as in Figs. 59 and 60.

In this case the band *a b* would seem to be widest at the front, gradually tapering towards the sides, as shown in the figure. This is because the band is practically on a section of a cone, the slant height of which is very oblique to the central ray, the opposite of the condition in the rim of the bowl.

Fig. 59

Another very important application of the apparent forms of circles is found in the drawing of rims and hoops, or raised bands. As to rims, we may have a vessel, as in Fig. 61. The rim would in this case present

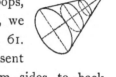
Fig. 60

a varying quantity from front to sides, and from sides to back. Thus, at the sides its thickness would not appear to be foreshortened in the least, as the line expressing its thickness would be at right angles to the rays of light to the eye: but, at the front and back, the reverse of this would *be true;* and the lines expressing the thickness would be proportionately foreshortened, provided the inner and the outer ellipses were in the same plane; but the front thickness, being nearer to the eye, would appear greater than the thickness at the back.

Fig. 61

The principle will be at once seen if we consider the rim to be one-quarter of the diameter across the top of the vessel (Fig. 62). Then we shall have to take a quarter from the ends of each diameter of the circle represented by the larger ellipse, and through these points draw the curve. *a* 1 and *b* 2, on the diameter *a b*, will be real quarters of the line; but on

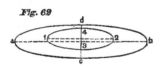
Fig. 62

the diameter *c d*, the real quarters being at unequal distances from the eye, the farthest *quarter* will appear much smaller than the nearest one. The quarter-points on the long diameter may be placed without trouble, but those on the shorter diameter are more liable to error.

The precise difficulty in this division will be hereafter considered. It will be readily understood, since the shorter diameter of the circle, *c d*, was divided into four equal parts, that there will be presented to the eye a series of diminishing quantities, the first or nearest of which will appear to be the largest, and the farthest will appear to be the smallest; so that we should have *a* $1 = b\, 2$, while *c* 3 would be greater than *d* 4. Hence the thickness of all rims having the faces at right angles to the axis appears greatest at the sides or at the ends of the major axis of the ellipse, and the rims appear thicker in front than on the back. Thus we have the rule for rims. *The apparent thickness of a rim at the ends of the short diameter bears the same proportion to the thickness at the ends of the long diameter as exists between the long and the short diameters themselves.*

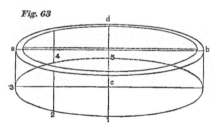

Fig. 63

The application of the foregoing analysis is required for a large class of objects (Fig. 63). Take a hoop, for instance: by the rule given, its upper rim is readily drawn; but the apparent varying depth of the hoop from top to bottom requires a new application of the same analysis. All difficulty will disappear if we draw the five vertical lines, 1, 2, 3, 4, 5, and note, that, by reason of their increasing remoteness, 1 is the longest, being nearest; while 2 is shorter than 1, and longer than either of the other three ; 3 is shorter than 2, longer than 4, and intermediate between 1 and 5 ; and 4 is shorter than 3 and longer than 5 ; 5 is the shortest of the series, because it is at the greatest distance.

Thus the five lines representing the same constant quantity appear unequal on account of their unequal distances from the eye.

A thoughtless pupil will always fail in these particulars, hence the necessity of thorough work on these points.

The rim is an element which will require some further explanation for its complete comprehension. Let c and c' be the center of two concentric circles. The intermediate space between the two circumferences is what we wish to draw. Placing the eye at E, let the circles be tipped obliquely, as in Fig. 64. Drawing the outer or tangential rays from the eye to the larger circle, we find the points of tangency to be a' and b': joining these two points by a straight line, we shall have the position of the major axis of the larger ellipse ; it will appear on the perspective plane at $a'' b''$. Now, if we join the points of tangency of the outer rays of the inner circle $d' e'$, we shall have the position of the major axis of the inner circle, seen in Fig. 64 on T P, at $d'' e''$.

From Fig. 64 it will be seen that the foreshortened diameter of the circle $n m$ and all its points and quantities, viz., $n o, o c, c r, r m$, will be obtained in their true proportions on the intersecting plane T P.

Now construct Fig. 65 by making $n''' o''' r''' m'''$ and $a''' d''' e''' b'''$ the same as the corresponding quantities in Fig. 64.

Draw the two ellipses in their respective positions, as indicated by these lines and points, and the true apparent form of the rim will be obtained, as seen through the transparent plane T P, from E. The principle here developed holds good in the apparent forms of all rings and rims whose surfaces reside in a single plane, and the application of the principle becomes very frequent in the drawing of models.

It will be apparent from the foregoing analysis, that, to draw a

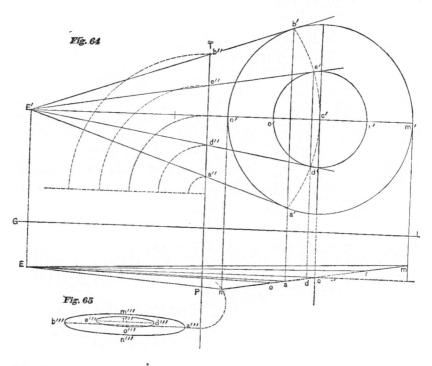

wheel in an oblique position, the hub can not be placed in the middle of the ellipse which represents the full size of the wheel, but must be pushed back of the apparent center of the wheel : the outer ellipse of the hub will be somewhat off the center, because it projects. If the hub is long, there would be another modification of the form; but, when the object is placed before the draughtsman, there is no trouble in reading the form by means of the explanation already given.

THE DRAWING OF ELLIPSES.

Ellipses seen in various positions appear under several modifications, some of which it is important to notice. First, an elliptical form, as for instance an elliptical dish, seen obliquely from a point in a plane which contains the shorter diameter of the ellipse (Fig. 66); that is, the eye and the shorter diameter of the ellipse being in the same vertical plane perpendicular to the longer diameter. The ellipse will appear to diminish in width, according to the degree of obliquity.

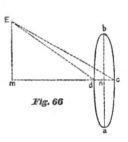

Fig. 66

Thus, let *a b* be an ellipse, *n m* being in the same plane as the ellipse; let E be the eye as far above that plane as *m* E. Then the diameter *a b* will not appear to be foreshortened, but will appear of its full length, while the

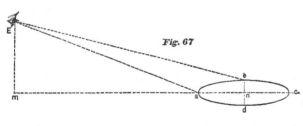

Fig. 67

shorter diameter *c d* will appear to be foreshortened; and, the nearer the eye is brought to *m*, the shorter will the line *c d* appear; the higher above *m* the eye is placed, the less foreshortened the line *c d* becomes. Again (Fig. 67), let *m* be a point in the extended plane of the ellipse *a b c d*, and E the position of the eye above the point *m*, at a distance equal to the line E *m*. Then *d e*, the shorter diameter, will not appear to be foreshortened; its true length being perpendicular to the central ray of light from itself to the eye. But *a c*, the longer diameter of the ellipse, one end being nearer to the eye than the other, becomes foreshortened; the amount of foreshortening depending upon the nearness of the eye to the point *m*. It will be observed, that to foreshorten the longer diameter of the ellipse, the shorter diameter remaining the same, will have the effect of bringing the ellipse more nearly to the form of a circle.

Fig. 68

It therefore follows, that if the longer diameter of an ellipse appears to be foreshortened, so as to make it seem just equal to the shorter diameter, the ellipse will appear to be a perfect circle, and must be so drawn.

It will be seen, that the apparent form of an elliptical dish might be represented as having a perfect circle for the outline of the upper ellipse. (See Fig. 68.)

DRAWING THE TRIANGLE AND TRIANGULAR FRAMES.

In drawing a triangle in an oblique position, it is only necessary to find by observation the apparent inclinations and lengths of the three lines, and to place them in their true positions, according to the reading of the *same*.

But, in relation to the triangular frame, there are a few points requiring notice, in order to secure ready execution and accurate work.

Let *a b* be the position of the lower or base front-line of a triangular frame standing upon a horizontal plane (Fig. 69). First find the apparent position of the central point of the line *a b*, by holding the pencil vertically against the apex of the triangle *c*, noticing where

the point *n* falls on *a b:* compare the length of *c n* with *a b*, and thus determine the point *c*. Draw *c n*, then *c a* and *c b*, completing the face of the triangular frame. Having determined their inclinations, draw *c e* and *a d*, observing that they are convergent lines : determine the amount of convergence, observe the length of *c e*, and draw *d e* convergent with *a c* in the direction of *c*. Now find the centers of the two sides *a c* and *c b*, at *o* and *p*, and

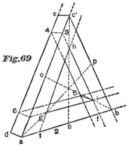

Fig.69

draw from each of these two points dotted lines to the opposite angles.

Determine the width of the frame as compared with the line *a b*. Let us suppose it to be one-sixth of that line : divide *a n*, half of the line *a b*, into three parts, so that each part will represent the apparent length of an equal third of the line *a n*, placing the points of these divisions at 1, 2. Draw from 1 the line 1 *h*, convergent with *a c*, in the direction of *c;* it will cut the vertical line *c n* in *h:* draw *h f*, convergent with *c b*, in the direction of *b;* draw the line *a p* bisecting the angle *c a b;* it will cut the line 1 *h* in *g:* draw *g i*, convergent with *a b*, in the direction of *b*. These lines will complete the right face of the frame.

Extend *f h* to the point 3, and draw 3 4, convergent with *c e* and *a d*, fixing the point 4. From 4 draw a dotted line convergent with *c b* and *h f*, and fix the point 5. From 5 draw the line 5 6 convergent with *a b* and *g i*, completing the inner visible surface of the frame.

The method here given for drawing the triangular frame in this position will sufficiently indicate the method to be pursued in all other possible positions. It is always important that the student should determine and keep in mind the different sets of convergent lines, always being sure to determine the direction of their convergence.

THE FRAME-CUBE.

Construct the outline as in the case of a solid cube, *a b* being the nearest vertical line (Fig. 70). In the first place determine how much of this line represents the apparent width of the vertical piece of the frame on the left side. If it is one-sixth, divide the line *a b* into as many equal parts, placing the points 1 2; now draw lines, both to the right and to the left, from each of these two points, convergent with

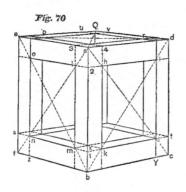

Fig. 70

a d and *b c*, and with *a e* and *b f* respectively: draw the diagonals *a f, a c, b e, b d*. These diagonals, cutting the lines drawn from 1 and 2 to the right and left, will determine the points *h, k, i, j, l, m, n, o*, from which complete the inner squares of the right and left faces of the frame. It will be observed, that, to secure all the varying dimensions of the framework, only one measurement need be determined; viz., *m x*, the apparent width of the nearest upright standard. From the determination of this one quantity, all the other remaining dimensions follow as a matter of course, by means of the diagonals, and of the converging

sets of lines.   Extend *m l* to 3, and *k h* to 4, and draw lines from 3
and from 4 convergent respectively with *a d* and *a e*.   Then draw the
diagonals of the upper face of the cube.   Where these diagonals cut
the lines from 3 and 4, fix the angles of the inner square, as in the
case of the two side faces, and complete the square.

Now draw from *n, m,* and *s* lines convergent with *b c,* and from
k, j, and *t* lines convergent with *b f:* draw vertical lines from *r* and *p,*
and also from *q, u,* and *v;* as far as visible.   If other inner lines of the
frame are visible, as, for instance, lines from *z* and *y,* they may be
represented with their proper convergence.   The drawing of the
frame-cube will not be found difficult if the method here indicated is
diligently followed.

With this model the danger is, that a pupil will undertake to guess
at some things without strictly observing them, and following the
order and method here laid down.   Such efforts will generally lead,
with a great loss of time, to an entire failure.

DRAWING THE SINGLE CROSS.

Let it be in either a vertical, horizontal, or an inclined position ;
first draw the squares,
a b c d,   d′ b′ c′ d′, and
d″ b″ c″ d″ (Figs. 71, 72,
and 73), to inclose the
cross in the several positions.   Next draw the diagonals to these squares,

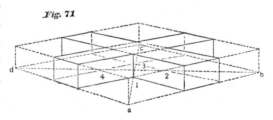

Fig. 71

and take the apparent middle division of one side of a square equal to·the thickness of the arms. From these points draw lines through the squares, parallel to the adjacent sides, cutting the diagonals in points 1, 2, 3, 4: through these points draw two lines parallel to, or converging with, the other two lines, as the case may be; this will

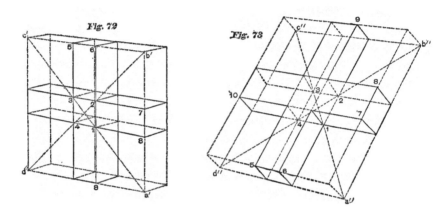

complete the face of the cross. Next, in a similar manner, draw lines from the points 5, 6, 7, 8, 9, 10, parallel or converging, to indicate the thickness of the cross, and then complete the drawing by the lines which make up the back face of the cross. Care must be taken to draw each line with its own system of parallels, and with its proper convergence, where there is any.

DRAWING THE DOUBLE CROSS.

The double cross naturally comes after the frame-cube, and it should be drawn at least in two positions. First place it with one shaft upright and the other two horizontal: draw, first, *a̅ b*, the nearest vertical of the upright shaft (Fig. 74). Compare the apparent thickness of either of the horizontal arms of the shaft with the line *a b*. Let us suppose it to be one-seventh : then divide the vertical line, *a b*, into seven equal parts ; and from points *a* and *b* marking the middle division, draw the lines 2 and 3, indicating the positions of the two horizontal arms, observing the true proportion, taking care to make the nearer longer than the farther arms.

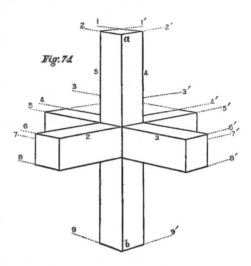

Fig. 74

Having drawn the lines 2 and 3, the inclination of every other line in the drawing will have been determined when the amount of convergence of the other lines has been fixed. Draw the two remaining vertical lines, 4 and 5, and the apparent form of the square on the upper end of the vertical shaft : then construct the two visible sides of the square at the lower end. In the same manner draw the visible ends of the horizontal shafts, and the two visible lines of the invisible squares of the same shafts. It will be seen that there will be, in this position of the double cross, two sets of convergent lines, nine lines in each set : one set, 1, 2, 3, 4, etc., will vanish to the left ; and the other set, 1', 2', 3', 4', etc., to the right. To draw this model in this and in the following position requires strict attention and close observation on the part of the student.

The next position in which we will suppose this model to be placed
will be that in which it rests upon three of its arms, one being directly
in front.   In this case we should draw first the line *a b*, indicating the
position of the arm, one end of which is nearest to us.   The line, we
will suppose, appears to be nearly vertical, leaning a little to the right.
Divide *a b* so as to get the central division, as in the last case, observing that the seven equal divisions of the line *a b* will present to the
eye a series of diminishing quantities from *b* to *a*, because the line is
receding.   Take the middle seventh for the thickness of the lateral
piece : draw, with their true inclinations, the lines *c* and *d*.   Observe
carefully, and make these arms in their true relative proportion
(Fig. 75).

Complete the figure by drawing all the subordinate lines, each converging with its own system.   In this case there will be three systems of convergence, with nine lines in each system.   It will be seen
that the lines *a b*, *c*, and *d* are lines belonging to the three different
systems of convergence ; and each may be considered the leading line
in its own system.   The first set of lines, converging upward, is 1, 2,
3, 4, etc. ; the second set, converging downward to the left, is 1′, 2′, 3′,
4′, etc.   The third set, converging downward to the right, is 1″, 2″,
3″, 4″, etc.   If the drawing has been accurately made, the curve of
an ellipse can be drawn through the eight points at the ends of the
four arms.   The curve may be lightly sketched, as an aid in the construction of the drawing.

Having studied the main principles of model-drawing from an
analysis of the geometrical conditions under which various forms
appear, these principles must be put into practice by the use of the
models.   For this purpose each model should be drawn carefully in

several positions. Practice should be kept up until the student is able to draw at sight any model in any possible position. No reliance whatever should be placed upon the practice of making

Fig. 75

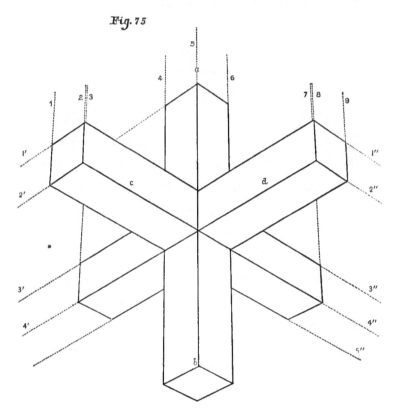

copies of drawings of models. It is only so much time thrown away. One might as well copy a poem in order to learn how to compose one. And, although copying pictures of models is at the present time much practiced in many of our public schools, I am satisfied that the pupils learn less and less of model-drawing as the practice continues.

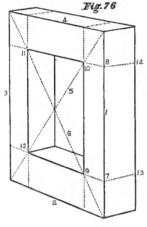

Fig. 76

We have already seen the use of the diagonals when drawing the frame-cube (Fig. 76). Take now the frame-square, and draw it in several positions, drawing the lines in the order of the numerals. Having placed the first six lines, fix the points 7 and 8 by comparing the width of the pieces of the frame with the line 1, and draw lines from them converging with 2 and 4. They will cut the diagonals in points 9, 10, 11, and 12: these points determine the inner lines of the frame (Fig. 77). Place the points 13 and 14 by drawing lines from 7 and 8 converging with the end-lines, which give the thickness: draw also the visible inner lines from 11 and 12 with the same convergence, if there is any in this set of lines. From 13 in the upright, and from 14 in the inclined figure, draw the visible line on the back side: this will cut the line from 11 or 12, and give the thickness on the inside. The remaining lines will follow in their appropriate

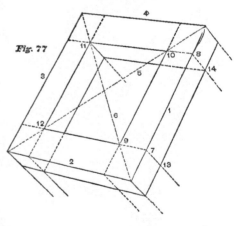

Fig. 77

places without any difficulty. The success of the drawing will depend upon following attentively the order here given. There is another application of the use of diagonals of a rectangle in sketching buildings, which we may notice here (Fig. 78).

Let us suppose we have drawn the vertical rectangle 1, 2, 3, 4, representing the end of a house, and that the gable, or point of the roof, is vertical with the real center of the rectangular end : by drawing the diagonals 5 and 6, we find the real center of the rectangle, and from it draw a vertical line ; the angle of the roof will be somewhere on this line. Find the altitude of the roof by comparison with line 1, and draw to the upper angles of the end-lines 8 and 9.

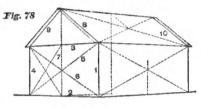

Fig. 78

As the roof projects over the ends, the line of the ridge can be drawn, and the projection made as indicated in the drawing. The center of the ground-plan, or of the front of the house, can be obtained in the same way, for the purpose of placing the front door, or any central feature ; and these rectangles can be divided into halves, quarters, and eighths, etc., by means of the diagonals, for the purpose of placing windows, or other features of the building.

Observe always that the intersection of the diagonals of a rectangle in any position, perspectively represented, *gives the real center of the rectangle, and not the apparent center.* The place of the chimney, if it is in the middle of the roof from one end to the other, can be placed by drawing the diagonals on the roof and through their intersection, drawing the line upward convergent with the ends of the roof 8 and 10 : this line will cut the ridge in the center.

Place the cube in two or three positions, and draw it at sight. First, in a vertical position, on a horizontal plane, a little below the

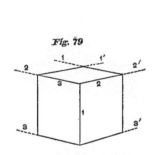

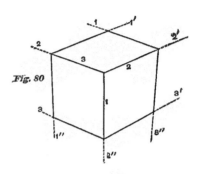

eye. There will be two sets of converging lines, with three lines in each set, 1, 2, 3, to the left, and 1′, 2′, 3′, to the right (Figs. 79 and 80).

Second, in an oblique position, drawing the lines in the order of the numbers, observing the three sets of converging lines, 1, 2, 3, and 1′, 2′, 3′, as in the figure above, and 1″, 2″, 3″, converging downward.

Third, place the model in a vertical position, showing the right or

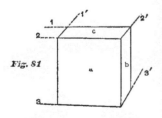

left side narrow (Fig. 81): draw the wide face first in its true proportion, taking especial care to make the narrow side no wider than it really appears. To do this, remember to compare the *horizontal* width, by means of the pencil held in the usual manner, with the length of the first vertical line drawn. Having drawn the narrow face *b*, and found the inclination of the lines 1, 2, 3, the face *c* is easily represented by drawing each of its further boundary-lines converging in their respective sets.

The four-sided prism should be drawn in several different positions,
taking care to note the sev-
eral systems of converging
lines and their directions
(Fig. 82). The amount of
convergence in all cases
should be determined by
close inspection of the models themselves, the degree
of convergence depending
on the distance of the eye.
The triangular prism may
be placed in a variety of
positions (Fig. 83). The

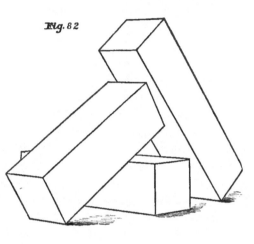

Fig. 82

altitude *c d* must be drawn after the base-line *a b*, remembering that the

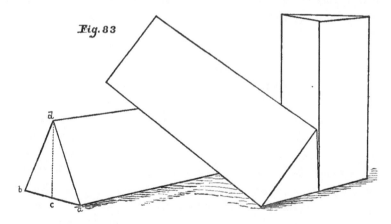

Fig. 83

nearer half of the base will appear the longer when the base *a b* is a retreating line, and that consequently the altitude *c d* must appear to be beyond the apparent center of *a b*.

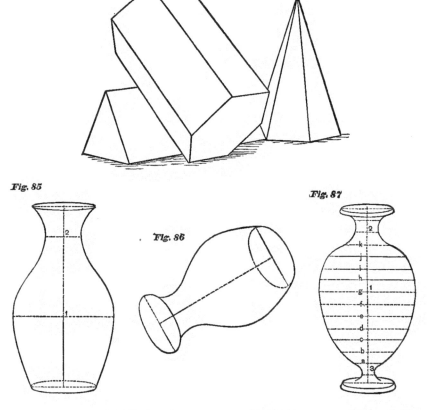

Fig. 84

Fig. 85

Fig. 86

Fig. 87

Place the hexagonal prism on the triangular prism, taking especial care to read according to the method we have indicated, observing all the sets of converging lines (Fig. 84).

Vases should be drawn in various positions (Fig. 85). Beginning
with the axis, find the proportionate lengths
and widths of the ellipses of the bases, and
determine the greatest and least diameter,
and the position of each on the axis, as
points 1 and 2, thus fixing the height of
each.

Observe the use of section lines at right
angles to the axis, in drawing symmetrical
figures (Figs. 86 and 87). As many may
be drawn as desired at equal or unequal
distances from each other, provided they are
always at right angles to the axis : they will
be bisected by the axis. In other words, the
two parts of these section lines will be equal.
See *a, b, c, d, e, f, g,* etc., in the illustration.

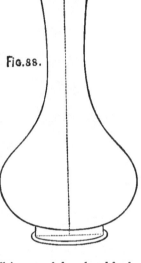

Fig.88.

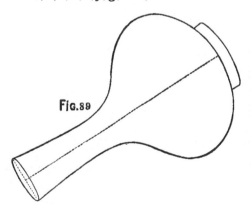

Fig.89

This model should be
drawn in two or three positions. First upright, and
then resting upon one side
(Fig. 88). The latter position will try the skill of the
pupil in reading correctly
the apparent form (Fig. 89).
Care should be taken to foreshorten the length in the
proper proportion. For this
purpose, compare the apparent length of the axis with the greatest

diameter; as one end of the axis is invisible, the pupil must imagine where on the surface of the model he could place a point that would cover the invisible end of the axis. Having drawn the axis in its apparent proportion with the greatest diameter, proceed to place the several apparent diameters, as in the preceding examples.

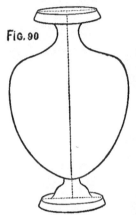

FIG. 90

This model is one of the more difficult ones of the series (Fig. 90). Its form, however, is based on the oval, which may be slightly modified in some parts of the outline. In any of these forms of vases, after the first sketch is made, *turn the drawing upside down to see if it is correctly drawn: any want of symmetry will thus be seen at once.*

LIGHT, SHADE, REFLECTED LIGHT, CAST SHADOW, AND REFLECTIONS.

The department of light and shade, with all its interesting modifications, approaches more nearly to what one might call real art, than the subjects hitherto discussed, which pertain to construction. But it will be found here, as well as everywhere else in art, that we are dealing with absolute law, and that there is no room for guess-work. There will be in this department ample chance for the exercise of close observation, quick apprehension of principles, and of great care and taste in execution.

Light, as we treat it, in respect to objects is of two kinds. First, direct light is that from the sun or from some other luminous body;

second, diffused light is that, which pervades, in the daytime, an ordinary room.

In the first form of light, the illuminated surfaces, parts in shade, and cast shadows will all possess mathematical proportions and definite limitations, and will have to be dealt with in reference to geometrical formulas. Light and shade in this kind of light is regarded as a part of Descriptive Geometry, and forms by itself a separate subject.

But the treatment of objects in the diffused light of a room is the subject of our present inquiry. In this light the appearance of objects will be quite different from that of the same objects in sunlight, and yet there is law pervading both classes of phenomena.

For the purpose of studying these effects, one should sit with the left shoulder to a window, the only source of light.

Take, first, the common white cube, and place it in front, at a convenient distance, say six feet or more, from the eye. If it be the first effort of the student to read light and shade, he will most likely not be able to see the nicer differences : he will have to learn *how* to *see.* For this purpose let the student close one eye, and then with the other half closed study attentively the light and shade upon the object : in order to see correctly, ample time must be given to this process ; the pupil sitting in this manner one, two, or five minutes, repeating the effort often, until all that is to be seen is fully apprehended.

First, it will be observed that a part of the surface of the cube is in light, and a part in shade. Let the student make with a pencil a very light sketch of the outline of the object. Shade with vertical lines the right face, which is in shadow, and then darken it with oblique cross-lines in one or two directions, and fill in the open checks with dots or dashes, to destroy or modify the netted appearance. Now it will be important to note the modifications of the shade on this side. It should be observed that it is not of a uniform depth over the whole face, but is darkest near the front edge, and at the upper part of the surface in front, at point A ; while it is lightest at the back

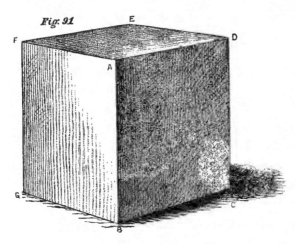

and lower part of the face near C (Fig. 91). This last modification results in part from light reflected from the plane on which it rests, and in part from its contrast with the darker cast shadow. The near part of the same face is darkened by contrast with the high light on the opposite side of the line A B. The illuminated left face will be lightest along the line A B, lighter at A than at B, and darker along the line F G, and darker at G than at F.

The top may be in a lower light than the right side, according to the position in reference to the light : it will be darkest along the line A F, and next to the illuminated face ; and lightest next to the dark side, along the line A D. It will be seen that the three faces of the cube, in this position, present a series of contrasts of light and shade, along the three lines running to the nearest solid angle, A. It is exactly in the order of these contrasts that the drawing is made to express relief, as will be seen hereafter.

It will be observed, that in Fig. 92 the proportion of light and shade on the three faces is exactly reversed; and, instead of appearing as a solid cube, the arrangement of light and shade shows that it represents a half of a hollow cube.

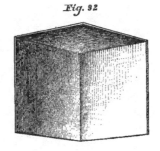

Fig. 92

In reference now to the cube (Fig. 91), we find that the following facts have been observed : —

First, On an illuminated plane, the highest light is on the nearest part of the plane.

Second, On a semi-illuminated plane, the deepest shade is adjacent to the illuminated plane.

Third, When a plane is in shadow, the deepest shade is on that part of the plane nearest the eye; and reflected lights would most likely appear on the more distant and lower part of the plane.

Fourth, The cast shadow is darker than the adjacent shaded surface of the object which cast it, and the darkest part of the shadow will always be nearest to the object casting it.

The principles developed above will be found applicable to all rectangular solids, and, with some modifications, to all objects on which light and shade may be conveniently studied. For however small the object, if no more than the thousandth of an inch in diameter, there would be the same facts of light and shade, high light, half-light, shaded surface, affected more or less by reflected light and cast shadow : so that an attentive study of the cube in light and shade will develop the principles of the whole system of distribution. Let the student study the cube in light and shade, and draw it until there is nothing more to learn from it.

For the next example in light and shade, let us take the cylinder, giving us a curved surface (Fig. 93).

Place the cylinder so that the light will fall upon it over the left

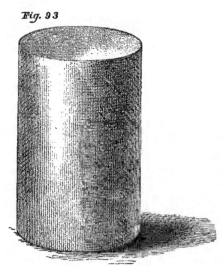

Fig. 93

shoulder, and observe the position of the lights, shades, reflected lights, and shadow. The deepest shade comes on the right side, a little way in from the outline : it is the darkest at the top, and, by reason of reflected light, less dark at the bottom. The highest light appears on the left side, a little way in from the outline : it is the lightest at the top. The upper base of the cylinder is in half-light, lightest next to the deepest shade on the right side, and darkest at the back and left. In this position neither the highest light nor the deepest shadow occurs at the outline of the model, as in the cube, where the highest light and the deepest shadow are contiguous. In natural scenery these contrasts frequently occur in juxtaposition.

In the study of the cube and cylinder we have become acquainted with many of the first principles of light and shade. We may now take up the sphere; and, since its apparent form is a circle from all points of observation, we may compare it with other objects whose apparent forms are represented by a circle such as the plane circle and the hollow hemisphere, the cone with the apex toward the eye, a hollow cone with the apex away from the eye, etc. For this purpose set up, if obtainable, these five objects, so that each will be represented in outline by a circle, and then, drawing five circles on the paper, proceed to study and represent the several forms, with all their nice modifications and distributions of light and shade. Nothing can be more useful than the faithful study of these objects.

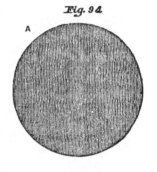

Fig. 94

A represents the flat shaded surface of a circle in nearly uniform tint (Fig. 94). B, the study of the light and shade of the sphere, as it appears to the pupil, with the high light on the upper

Fig. 95

left-hand side, but a little in from the outline of the circle (Fig. 95). The deepest shadow is seen on the lower right side, but not darkest near the outline: reflected light is seen on the shaded side, caught up from the plane on which it rests. The cast shadow on the plane would be, as far as visible, in the form of an ellipse.

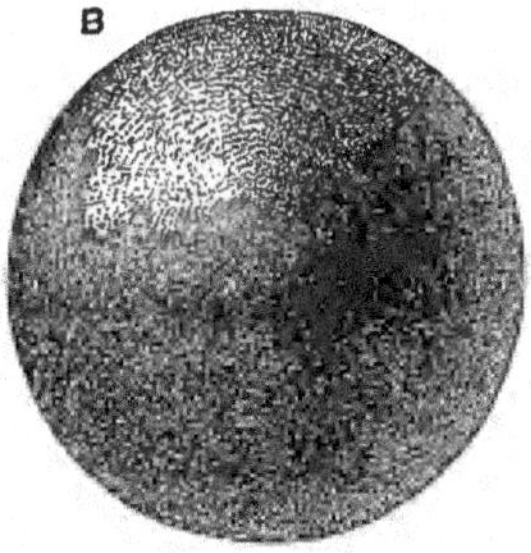

C represents the hollow hemisphere (Fig. 96). Its shaded surface, in a proper light, is a cast shadow thrown upon the inner surface by the rim: it has, therefore, the disposition of a cast shadow, with reflected light which belongs to a shaded surface.

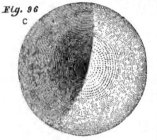
Fig. 96

D represents the cone, with the apex towards the eye (Fig. 97). The deepest shade will appear under the apex on the shaded side, the highest light being on the opposite side of the apex. It will be observed that near the base, on the light side, it must be slightly shaded; and that near the base, on the shaded side, it must be less darkly shaded than under the apex: so that, as we approach the base from the apex, there is less difference between the light and the shaded side than there is near the apex. Fix clearly the fact that *both the light and the shade are focussed near the apex, on exactly opposite sides.*

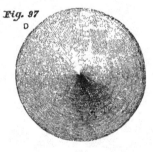
Fig. 97

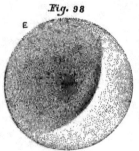
Fig. 98

E represents the hollow cone (Fig. 98). Notice how all the conditions of the distribution of light and shade are reversed from those in the cone.

The means to be employed in representing light, shade, and shadow are various: the selection may be made according to the preference of the teacher or pupil. We may use the pen and ink, lead-pencil, crayon-point, charcoal-point, and stump with charcoal or crayon, or the brush with India ink, or with any monochrome.

When lines are used, they should be laid as evenly as possible, and with nice gradation in passages of varying depth. Flat tint should be laid with one set of lines running in the same direction: where only one set is used, it is called half-tint (Fig. 99). If more depth is required, two or more sets of lines may be used: the different sets should cross each other at an acute angle, as in the illustra-

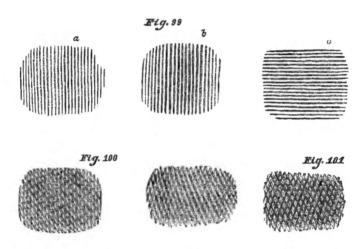

Fig. 99

Fig. 100

Fig. 101

tion, Fig. 100. This process is called *hatching*. The lines should not be drawn far at one stroke of the pencil: it is better to lift the pencil as often as is convenient. A rather broad line is much better than a fine, wiry line; and the spaces between lines should be uniform, and not wider than the lines themselves. Vertical lines are appropriate for vertical plane surfaces, and horizontal lines for horizontal surfaces. Straight lines should be used for plane, and curved lines for curved, surfaces; or both may be used on the surface of the cylinder and cone, where the surfaces are both straight and curved, but in different directions.

Stippling, with dots between the lines in the open checks, may be resorted to, in order to produce a uniform effect, and to cause the lines to blend (Fig. 101).

Fig. 102   *Fig. 103*

The study of shading should be pursued by drawing and shading as many vases and other objects as possible (Figs. 102 and 103). There is no danger that the student will draw too many, or become too familiar with these objects. After each study of a model, a rapid drawing entirely from memory should be made. When completed, it may be compared with the original drawing to test its accuracy. This practice is of the greatest value in fixing in the mind whatever knowledge has been acquired in the study of objects.

REFLECTIONS.

Reflections are an important element in pictorial effect, and, in connection with model-drawing, should receive a passing notice.

First, they are produced by a polished surface taking up the light of an object, and conveying it to the eye. If an object, such as a cube, is placed upon a polished table, there will be present all the various modifications of light, shade, and shadow; and, in addition to these, they will all be reproduced in the reflection of the object, with some exceptions and modifications. The cast shadow will, however, never be fully reproduced in the reflection; because, in this position of the cube, the shadow rests upon the plane of reflection: hence the cast shadow will be modified in proportion to the perfection of the reflecting surface.

A vertical line reflected by a horizontal plane surface will always give a vertical reflection. See, in Fig. 104, *a*, with *a'* as the reflection on the reflecting plane D E ; but *a'* will be shorter than *a*, according as the eye is more or less above the plane of reflection, if measured in the usual way by holding up the pencil. A line inclined to the right, but not to the front or back, as *b*, will have its reflection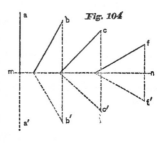
more inclined, as the eye is at a greater distance above the plane of reflection, as at *b' : e* and *f* will have their reflections *e'* and *f'*

respectively. These statements may be easily verified by holding a pencil in various positions against the face of a looking-glass, noticing the position of the reflection in each case. In the Fig. 104 the line *m n* is perpendicular to the central ray of light from the object to the eye.

These statements will guide the student in his observations of the facts in sketching, as he can amplify them in many ways. When once the general principle is apprehended, there will be no further difficulty in its application to all the modifications under which reflections may occur.

There is another class of reflections with which the student will have to become familiar; and that is, where the objects themselves are more or less polished, giving reflecting surfaces, which catch up lights and colors from any illuminated objects near them, producing numerous modifications of all the lights and shades hitherto noticed. The only law which governs this class of reflections, as, indeed, all others, is, that the *angle of reflection is always equal to the angle of incidence;* and the position of a reflected light on a polished object, as on a polished silver or glazed earthen vase, will be determined by the position of the object which is the source of the light reflected by the object. Thus, let A, Fig. 105, be a plan of a polished cylinder, with the eye at E: let B, at the same distance from the object as E, be the source of the light reflected from the surface; E B being in a plane perpendicular to the surface of the cylinder. To find the point of illumination, draw lines from E and B to the point *a'*, making equal angles with the circumference at that point: *a'* will be the point illuminated, because lines drawn from the point *a'* to E and B will make equal angles with the arc at that point. These lines would also make equal angles with the tangent of the arc at a'. This is easily done where the point of light and the eye are equally distant from the center of the cylinder ; but, where they are unequally distant, it becomes a difficult problem to find the *locus* of reflection. (See Appendix A.)

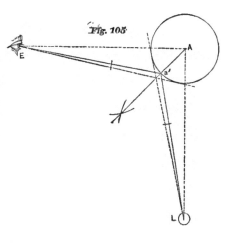

Fig. 105.

As these reflections are subjects of observation rather than of construction, it will be sufficient in this connection merely to indicate the law which governs them.

There is no class of phenomena more interesting or captivating to the painter than reflections and reflected light. To the landscape artist they are the source of some of his most pleasing effects. So much is he dependent upon reflections in water for entertaining the observer of his works, that a landscape picture without water is often devoid of interest ; while a very simple view with water, with its multitude of glancing lights and fragmentary shadows, becomes at once pleasing and delightful.

Reflections multiply the quantities which make up the rhythmical and harmonic series from which the mind derives its pleasure, and seem to suggest the idea of life and activity.

APPENDIX.

THE FOLLOWING IS THE SOLUTION OF THE PROBLEM FOR FINDING THE POINT
OF REFLECTED LIGHT ON A POLISHED CYLINDER.

THE following problem depends for its solution upon finding, upon the surface of a polished cylinder, a point where the angle of incidence from the light will be equal to the angle of reflection from the point to the eye.

To find the place of the point of illumination on a polished cylinder, when the place of the light and the place of the eye are given : —

The problem assumes four different forms.

First, When the point of light and the eye are in a plane not at right angles to the axis of the cylinder, and are equally distant from the cylinder.

Second, When the plane, in which the eye and light are located, is not at right angles to the axis of the cylinder, and the points of the eye and light are unequally distant from the cylinder.

Third, When the eye and light are in a plane perpendicular to the axis of the cylinder, and equally distant from the cylinder.

Fourth, When the plane, in which the eye and light are located, is perpendicular to the axis of the cylinder, and the point of the eye and light are unequally distant from the cylinder.

The first and second forms of the problem are not of easy solution. The third form is solved by drawing tangents from the points of the eye and light E and L, to the circumference of the cylinder on the near side, and by bisecting the angle formed by the two tangents : the bisecting line cutting the center of the cylinder will also cut the circumference at the point of illumination.

The fourth form of the problem is not so easy of solution, and it seems that it can only be solved in the following manner : —

Let E and L be the points of the eye and light at unequal distances from the cylinder A : draw several concentric circles B, D, G, etc. Draw tangents to

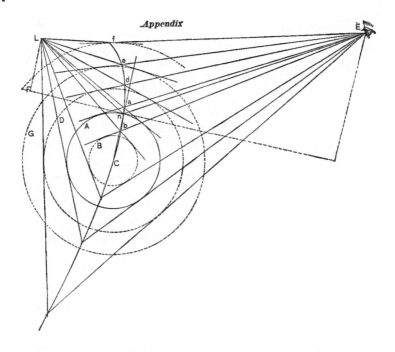

Appendix

the circumference of the cylinder and to each of the concentric circles ; each pair of tangents intersecting each other in *a, b, d, e, f.* Now, by constructing a curve passing through these several points of the intersecting pairs of tangents, the curve will cut the circumferences in the points of illumination, and will pass through the center of the cylinder. This curve will cut the surface of the cylinder in the point of illumination : for we shall find that the angles formed by lines drawn from these points of the curve, intersecting the concentric circles, will form equal angles with the circumferences of the circles at the points of intersection of the curve; thus showing that the angle of incidence is equal to the angle of reflection. Or, in other words, the lines drawn from L and E to these several points on the circumferences, found by the intersecting curve, will make equal angles with tangents drawn through the same points; thus proving that the angles of incidence and reflection are equal, and showing that the point found by the construction of the curve is the point of illumination, the locus of reflection.

NOTE 1. — The curve becomes a curve of the fourth degree by virtue of the arrangement of the points through which it passes.

NOTE 2. — If tangents are drawn to the same concentric circles on the far side of the cylinder, and the curve extended through the intersections of the tangents, the curve will give the points of illumination on the inner surfaces of cylinders arranged in place of the circles. There would seem to be no other simple solution of this problem that could be worked out visible to the eye.

www.ingramcontent.com/pod-product-compliance
Ingram Content Group UK Ltd.
Pitfield, Milton Keynes, MK11 3LW, UK
UKHW041326181224
3750UKWH00014B/98